WHERE
TO
LAUNCH
YOUR
BOAT

A selective guide to launching sites in England, Scotland and Wales

Compiled and edited by
Diana Goatcher
assisted by Wendy Robinson

WHERE TO LAUNCH YOUR BOAT

a selective guide to
launching sites in England,
Scotland and Wales

Compiled and edited by
Paul Gauthier
Illustrated by Wendy Robinson

Barnacle Marine

Contents

Barnacle Marine Ltd.
Blomfield Place
25 St. Botolph's Street
Colchester
Essex CO2 7EA

First edition 1986
Second edition 1988
Third edition 1990

ISBN 0 948 788 33 X

Cover design by Prepart of Colchester

Typeset by SB Datagraphics Ltd. Colchester, Essex.

Printed by Spottiswoode Ballantyne Ltd, Colchester, Essex.

Cover photographs, left to right.
'Winkle Brig' cruiser launching at Mylor Harbour, near Falmouth. Photograph supplied by the builders, Ferry Boatyard, Fiddlers Ferry Yacht Haven, Penketh, Cheshire.

Chris Craft from Bexley Boat Imports preparing to launch into the River Thames at The Embankment, Putney. Photographer: Joe McCarthy.

Whilst every care has been taken in the compilation of this guide no responsibility can be taken for the existence of any inaccuracies contained in the information. A reference to any particular site in this book is not evidence of a right of way to the site or of public availability at any time and the inclusion of any slipway in this book cannot be taken as a recommendation of such a site. The publishers do not hold themselves responsible for any accident which arises as the result of any slipway mentioned in this book being used.

A catalogue containing details of Stanfords Allweather Charts, and other nautical publications is available from the publishers.

INTRODUCTION

There are tens of thousands of small boat owners, many of whom are not members of clubs but who like to visit different areas of the country taking their boat with them. But where to launch? Good sites are not always easy to find. This book will guide you to over 930 sites throughout England, Wales and Scotland where you can launch your boat, whether it be a trailer-sailer, ski boat, sailing or fishing dinghy, runabout or inflatable.

The book is divided geographically into seven sections covering coastal sites with one section totally devoted to over 300 inland sites. Each section is prefaced by a map to enable the reader to quickly identify the location of sites.

Where possible, the following details are given for each site: the location together with detailed directions for getting there; the type of slipway and times when it can be used: in the case of tidal sites availability will refer to high water (HW); availability of fuel, parking (a charge is indicated by (c)), toilets, chandlers, boatyard and other facilities. Where possible details of speed limits or other restrictions which may be in force at a site are given together with an indication of the suitability of the site for a particular watersport or type of boat. In most cases a phone number is given and it is highly recommended that anyone intending to use a particular site should check for its availability and suitability for their particular requirements before setting off. If there is a charge for using the site this is indicated in the text by "Charge" at the end of the entry: charges are generally highest at the privately owned sites at boatyards and marinas but the facilities offered at these sites are usually excellent.

Most sites described are suitable for craft up to 18'LOA (5.5m) unless specified. A site described as suitable for dinghies only usually has restricted access which may mean that the boat has to be manhandled into the water. The hours of use given for coastal sites are intended as a guide only; obviously this is a matter which very much depends on the type of craft to be launched and on the conditions prevailing at the time. In the case of larger craft, especially those with a deep draught, launching should be undertaken as near HW as possible although at some exposed sites sea conditions at HW can be dangerous. Many sites can be used to launch smaller craft at most stages of tide, especially if the trailer can be manhandled across the beach to the water. Before launching you should always make sure that you are aware of any restriction which may be in force: this particulary applies to those wishing to launch powerboats or to water-ski. In many popular bathing areas, these activities are restricted to clearly defined areas and there are heavy penalties for infringement of the bye-laws: those wishing to water-ski should always be aware of the danger which they can present to bathers. In many harbours, especially on the south coast, a harbour due is charged which may be quite substantial and on most rivers and canals, a licence is required. Details of such requirements are given in the descriptive paragraph about each harbour.

It is advisable to find out about local conditions, especially on exposed coasts before launching. Often the Harbour Master or local Sailing Club Secretary can give advice and where possible the address or phone number of such people has been supplied. In addition there is a list of addresses at the end of the book which may be of use. When going offshore, always listen to the local forecast and remember that both onshore and offshore winds on any coast can be dangerous, especially near HW or when wind is against tide. Boats going offshore, no matter how far, should always carry a chart and compass, flares, an anchor and line and auxiliary propulsion if only oars and paddles: lifejackets or buoyancy aids should always be worn. At many sites there is a requirement for basic safety equipment to be carried and for proof of third party insurance to be shown before launching is permitted.

If you know of a suitable site which you feel should be included in this guide or have any comments about sites which are already included please write to the Editor, Barnacle Marine Ltd. Blomfield Place, 25 St. Botolph's Street, Colchester, C02 7EA

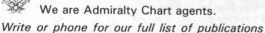

TRAILERS AND THE LAW

So often the trailer is the neglected part of the boating package. Whilst hulls, engines and other equipment are well maintained the trailer sits idly by, open and unprotected, and usually without even a squirt of grease. However the moment the sun appears it is hitched up with its load and expected to perform perfectly in delivering its charge to the water's edge. Do give it a chance. Protect those bearings with grease and put a dab on the ballhitch. Check the tyres and lights and above all make sure you are legal. Our trailer laws have now been brought in line with other EEC countries and to stop your weekend being marred by a brush with the police you must conform.

Braking Regulations

Trailers without brakes

You may use an unbraked trailer with a gross weight (trailer, boat and contents), of up to 750kg (15cwt), provided the towing vehicle kerbside weight is at least twice the gross weight of the trailer. All unbraked trailers must be clearly marked with their maximum gross weight, and it is an offence to load the trailer with more then its gross weight.

Trailers fitted with brakes

The braking system on new trailers must comply with the EEC directive that states that trailers must be fitted with a coupling and correctly matched brakes and linkage which have a minimum braking efficiency of 45% G. From April 1989, all new trailers must be fitted with auto-reverse brakes. A trailer must have a parking brake capable of holding the trailer stationary on a gradient of 18%. Good trailer centres can check the efficiency of your brakes for you.

Trailer Dimensions

The maximum width of a trailer when being towed by a motor car or light goods vehicle is 2.3m. In all other cases (HGV) this is 2.5m. The trailer or trailer load must not extend more than 305mm outwards on either side of the towing vehicle. The maximum width allowable, without police advice and supervision is 2.9m. A trailer and its load must not normally exceed 7 metres in length excluding drawbar and coupling. Longer loads are permissible for heavy vehicles conforming to certain conditions.

Lighting Regulations

Two red tail lights and brake lights must be fitted which operate with the towing vehicle lights. Two amber indicators must flash in unison with towing vehicle indicators. Two red triangular reflectors of the approved type must be fitted to all trailers and the number plate area must be illuminated. Trailers exceeding 5m in length must be fitted with orange side-facing reflectors and if a trailer is over 1.6m wide, white front marker lights are required. The latter are also required if trailer or load project more than 400mm beyond the outer edge of the front position lamps of the towing vehicle. At least one rear fog lamp must be fitted operating independently of the rear brake lights.

This is only a brief outline of the more important points of law affecting trailers. We are indebted to Indespension Ltd for their co-operation in preparing this section. We strongly recommend the purchase of their complete guide to trailers and towing "Trailer Manual" which is available, price £3.50 plus £1.00 postage and packing from Indespension Ltd, Belmont Road, Bolton, BL1 7AQ.

British Marine Industries Federation Slipways Award Scheme

The British Marine Industries Federation has set up an award scheme aimed at highlighting particulary good examples of slipways or other simple facilities provided to enable people to launch boats and "Get Afloat" easily and cheaply.

The purpose of the award is to encourage Authorities and others to widen and improve opportunities for people - young people and families in particular - to enjoy boating as economically as possible.

Barnacle Marine Ltd, publishers of the book "Where to Launch Your Boat" are sponsoring the award in co-operation with the Boating Facilities Service of the BMIF.

The scheme is open in the first place to Local Authorities, River Authorities and commercial boatyards who have commissioned or upgraded slipways or other launching facilities for small boats during the period ending 30th September in any year. The project judged to be the best will win the year's "Get Afloat Award" which will take the form of a new Mirror Dinghy. The presentation takes place during the London Boat Show in January with due ceremony, when the Dinghy will go to the Organisation nominated by the Mayor or leader of the winning Authority, and when a suitably inscribed plaque will also be presented.

Authorities are invited to submit drawings, photos and other details of schemes including a small scale map showing location by September 30th. This timing will allow for judging and the announcement of the winner(s) in time for the award ceremony at the London International Boat Show. Entries will be judged by the BMIF and the Award scheme will cover both tidal and inland launching facilities and will be included in Barnacle Marine's launching guide "Where to Launch Your Boat".

Those wishing to enter the award scheme, or put forward a slipway facility should contact The Secretary, Boating Facilities Service, BMIF. Boating Industry House, Vale Road, Weybridge, Surrey. KT13 9NS.

Help crew a lifeboat

Join the R.N.L.I. today.

It costs a staggering £100,000 a day to run Britain's lifeboats.

And incredible though it seems, a lifeboat somewhere is called out, on average, every 2½ hours.

That's why over 1,500 lives were saved at sea last year.

Since we rely entirely on voluntary contributions to stay afloat, your support will certainly play its part.

For the modest sum of £6 you can become a member.

To: The Director, R.N.L.I., West Quay Road, Poole, Dorset BH15 1HZ. I wish to join the R.N.L.I. My subscription rate is indicated below.
Shoreline Member £6 p.a. ☐ Joint Membership (Husband/Wife) £9 p.a. ☐
Governor £20 p.a. ☐ Life Governor (once only payment) £200 or more ☐

I enclose my subscription and/or donation of £ _____

Name _____

Address _____

_____ Postcode _____

Royal National
Lifeboat
Institution   X/12

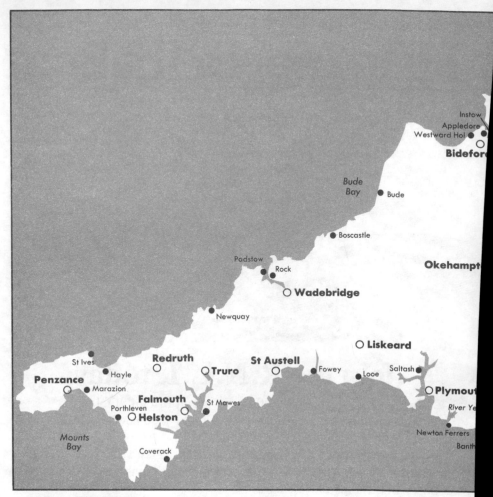

GLOUCESTERSHIRE

Beachley Point (Severn Estuary)
Car Ferry Slipway
Follow signs to Beachley from A 48 at Tutshill near Chepstow. Brick ex car ferry slipway
under Severn Bridge available for launching for 4 hours either side HW. No fuel, limited
parking for car and trailer. No speed limit: water-skiing allowed. Boats launching here
should notify the Authorities and ensure they are adequately powered; tidal currents of
10-12 knots are common here. No Charge.

Lydney Docks (Severn Estuary)
Lydney Yacht Club
From A 48, follow signs from Lydney Town to Industrial Estate and continue along
Harbour Road. Concrete slipway available for 2 hours either side HW. No fuel, limited
parking for car and trailer. No speed limit: water-skiing allowed. Boats launching here
should notify the Authorities and ensure they are adequately powered; tidal currents of
10-12 knots are common here. Use with permission of Yacht Club. Charge.

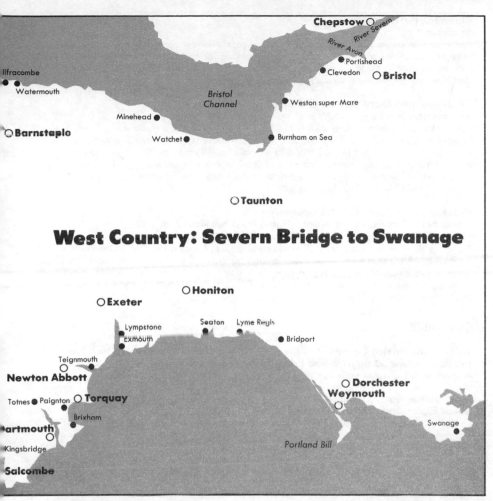

West Country: Severn Bridge to Swanage

AVON

Bristol (River Avon)
Bristol Marina, Albion Road
Follow signs to "SS Great Britain" from city centre: access is via Cumberland Rd and Hanover Place. Wide concrete slipway into deep water of Floating Harbour suitable all types of craft. Fuel, parking for car and trailer, toilets and chandlery, crane available for hire. Speed limit 6mph in harbour, 4mph in canal and river; for water-skiing contact marina office Tel Bristol(0272) 213198. Navigation licence required. Charge and harbour dues payable.

Bristol (River Avon)
Baltic Wharf Leisure Centre, Cumberland Road
Follow signs to dock area from city centre: access is via Cumberland Rd and through Underfall Yard, where the Harbour Office is located. Concrete slipway into min 3' water in Floating Harbour available from 0900- sunset daily except Christmas Day and suitable craft up to 18'LOA. Parking for car and trailer and toilets on site; chandlers and fuel ($\frac{1}{4}$ mile). Speed limit 6mph in harbour, 4mph in canal and river. Check in advance for availability Tel Bristol(0272) 297608. Navigation licence required and available from Leisure Centre. No Charge.

Clevedon (Bristol Channel)
Seafront

Leave M 5 at junction 20: site is 50yds west of pier. Narrow concrete slipway can be used at most states of the tide. Fuel in town, parking for car and trailer (c) and toilets on site. Speed limit inshore: water-skiing permitted offshore. Site is most suitable for dinghies, but can be used by small powerboats. No Charge.

Weston-super-Mare (Bristol Channel)
Knightstone Harbour

Leave M 5 at junction 21 and take A 370 to town centre, turning right at sea front. Site is at north end of town near Knightstone Point and Marine Lake. Concrete slipway available for 2 hours either side HW and suitable for all craft. Fuel in town, parking for car and trailer close by, toilets. Speed limit 5mph in harbour between the Pier and Knightstone Pt: water-skiing permitted outside this area, contact local club Tel Weston-super-Mare(0934) 515595. No Charge.

Weston-super-Mare (Bristol Channel)
Uphill Boat Centre, Uphill Wharf (Uphill Boat Services Ltd)

Follow A 370 south through town and turn off to Uphill 100yds past Uphill Garage. Concrete slipway available from 2½ hours before to 1½ hours after HW and suitable all craft up to 48'LOA and 18' wide. Fuel, parking for car and trailer, toilets, chandlery and boatyard facilities all on site. Water-skiing in Weston Bay. Additional facilities offered include pontoon moorings and boat storage. Check for availability Tel Weston-super-Mare(0934) 418617. Charge.

SOMERSET

Tides in the Bristol Channel can be very strong and may reach up to 5 knots outside Minehead Bay on ebb tides. This area is recommended for fairly experienced dinghy sailors only: if in doubt, seek local advice.

Burnham-on-Sea
South Esplandade (Bristol Channel)

Leave M 5 at junction 22 and follow signs to Burnham-on-Sea: site is at south end of Esplanade at the end of Pier St. Concrete and wooden slipway available for 2 hours either side HW and suitable all craft up to 3 tons max (incl trailer). Fuel, parking for car and trailer (c), toilets. Speed limit 10mph: water-skiing allowed offshore*. Permit must be obtained from Sedgemoor DC, Manor Gardens, Manor Rd. No Charge.

* Local water-skiing club operates a ski school at weekends, weather and tide permitting. Further information from Mr R J Larder Tel(0458) 35204 (daytime) or 47682 (evening).

Watchet (Bristol Channel)
Harbour Slipway

Follow A 39 from Bridgewater or A 358 from Taunton to Williton and turn off to Watchet. Concrete slipway availablle for 2 hours either side HW suitable all types of craft up to 30'LOA. Fuel from Williton (2 miles), parking for car and trailer in Market St (c), toilets and chandlery on site. Local Boat Owners Assoc has boat compound and welcomes visitors. Speed limit 5mph: no water-skiing. Contact Harbour Master Tel Watchet(0984) 31264. Charge and harbour dues payable.

Minehead (Bristol Channel)
Harbour Slipway

Follow A 358 from Taunton to Williton then A 39. Concrete slipway onto sand available for 2 hours either side HW suitable all craft up to 30' LOA. Fuel (½ mile), parking for car and trailer (c), toilets nearby and chandlers. Speed limit 5mph; water-skiing is permitted in the bay. Local Boat Owners Assoc has boat compound and welcomes visitors. Contact Harbour Master Tel Minehead(0643) 2566. Charge and harbour dues payable.

DEVON

Watermouth (Bristol Channel)
Watermouth Harbour
Follow A 39/A 399 from Barnstaple; harbour is 4 miles east of Ilfracombe opposite Watermouth Castle. Concrete slipway onto hard surface available at HW for large craft or at all states of tide for dinghies. Fuel, parking for car and trailer nearby, toilets at Watermouth YC, nearest chandlers at Ilfracombe. Speed limit 3 knots in harbour; water-skiing is allowed outside the harbour. Charge.

Ilfracombe (Bristol Channel)
Harbour Slipway
Follow A 361 from Barnstaple or signs to Ilfracombe from Blackmoor Gate. Concrete slipway onto hard sand available for 2½ hours either side HW for larger boats or at all times for dinghies. Diesel, parking for car and trailer (c), toilets, chandlery from Harbour Chandlery and Marine, boatyard facilities from Ilfracombe Marine Services. Speed limit 5 knots in harbour. Contact Harbour Master before launching Tel Ilfracombe (0271) 62108. **Note:** The slipway must be kept clear at all times to allow access to lifeboat. Charge.

Taw and Torridge Estuary
The estuary forms a large area of sheltered water extending from Barnstaple, at the head of the Taw estuary to Bideford, at the end of the Torridge estuary. There is a speed limit of 7 knots in the estuary, with water-skiing permitted in designated areas for 3 hours either side of HW but not from slipways.

Instow (River Torridge)
Instow Promenade
Off A 39 Bideford to Barnstaple road on east side of River Torridge. Two concrete slipways onto the sandy beach available for 3 hours either side HW suitable mainly for launching dinghies and small powerboats. Diesel, parking for car and trailer (20yds) (c), toilets in car park, outboard repairs from Instow Marine Services. Contact Harbour Master Tel Instow (0271) 860578. No Charge.

Bideford (River Torridge)
Bank End Slipway
Follow A 39 west from Barnstaple and turn left after crossing the high-level bridge to west bank of the River Torridge. Concrete slipway onto soft mud available for 1½ hours either side HW. No fuel, parking for car and trailer on site, toilets in Victoria Park, chandlery from R.N.S. Marine, 25b Fore St, Northam (4 miles). No Charge.

Appledore (River Torridge)
Ferry Slip, Appledore Quay
Follow A 39 west from Barnstaple, turning off in Bideford onto the A 386. Concrete slipway onto firm mud available for 2 hours either side of HW. No fuel, nearest car park in Odun Road but no boats or trailers allowed, toilets in Marine Parade, chandlery from The Sea Chest, 10 Market St. Site can be congested. No Charge.

Westward Ho! (Barnstaple Bay)
Slipway
From Bideford follow A 386 north to Northam and B 3236 west to Westward Ho! Concrete slipway onto sand available at all states of tide for dinghies. No fuel, parking for car (no trailers allowed), toilets, chandlery from R.N.S.Marine, Northam (2 miles). Launching from this slipway can be difficult at HW when there may be a heavy breaking sea. No Charge.

CORNWALL

Bude (Bude Bay)
Bude Harbour
Follow A 39 south from Barnstaple or B 3254/A 3072 from Launceston. Slipway is near lock at entrance to Bude Canal and access is down the breakwater along a narrow road. Stone and concrete slipway is available for up to 2 hours either side HW. Fuel from garage (¼ mile), parking for car and trailer (c)(400yds), toilets (¼ mile). Low speed in the harbour; no water-skiing in harbour or near beaches. **Note:** conditions at Bude can often prevent launching and entry to and exit from the harbour: seek local advice or consult the Harbour Master Tel Bude(0288) 3111. Charge.

Boscastle
Harbour Slip
Turn off A 39 onto B 3263: site is at top of harbour. Concrete slipway available for 2 hours either side HW. Petrol, parking for car and trailer (c), toilets. Speed limit 3 knots: water-skiing allowed offshore. Apply to Harbour Master for assistance. Charge.

Camel Estuary
The estuary extends for about eight miles inland, with Padstow standing about 2½ miles from the mouth and Wadebridge, which can be reached by small boats at HW, a further five miles SE. The sheltered waters of the estuary provide an excellent area for sailing, windsurfing and water-skiing. There is a speed limit in certain areas and especially through the moorings and in the channel from Padstow Harbour pierheads downstream to Ship-me-Pumps Pt. Water-skiing is permitted in designated areas upstream: details can be obtained from the Rock Sailing Club Tel Trebetherick(020 886) 2431 or Padstow Harbour Office on South Quay Tel Padstow(0841) 532239. All craft must pay harbour dues and all skiers must register with and become temporary members of Rock SC. Sailboarding is also restricted to certain areas: further details as above. In the summer this area becomes very crowded and manoeuvring space close to the slipways is severely limited.

Rock (River Camel)
Rock Sailing Club Slip, The Quay
Turn off A 39 at Wadebridge, taking B 3314 and minor roads to Rock, on the east shore opposite Padstow. Concrete slipway onto sandy beach available 2 hours either side of HW for a direct launch, otherwise for about 4 hours either side of HW. Fuel, parking for car and trailer (c), toilets at Rock SC, chandlery from Rock Watersports and Marine Services. This slip is busy at HW during the peak season. Vehicles are not allowed to park on the beach or slipway. Further information Tel Trebetherick(020 886) 2431. No Charge but harbour dues payable.

Rock (River Camel)
Ferry Point Slip
Follow A39 from Bideford, turning off onto B 3314 and minor roads: access is through public car park. Small wooden slip onto a sandy beach is available at all states of tide for small, light craft. No vehicles are allowed on the beach. Fuel, parking for car and trailer, toilets and chandlery nearby. No Charge but harbour dues payable.

Wadebridge (River Camel)
Bradford Quay
Turn off A 39 at head of Camel Estuary: site is just south of bridge. Concrete slipway available for 2 hours either side HW. Fuel, parking for car and trailer (c). Charge and harbour dues payable.

Padstow (River Camel)
Sailing Club Slip, West Quay
Follow A 39 from Bideford, then A 389 west of Wadebridge: site is adjacent Harbour Office. Concrete slipway is steep and fairly narrow with no winch and therefore suitable for light open boats up to about 17'LOA only; site is available 3 hours either side HW. Diesel from Harbour Commissioners' tank, petrol from garage in town, parking (c) on West Quay is often full (one trailer space), toilet, chandlery from Net Tec Marine Ltd, South Quay. No Charge but harbour dues payable.

Padstow (River Camel)
Iron Horse Slip, North Quay
Follow A 39 from Bideford, then A 389 west of Wadebridge. Concrete slipway into Outer Basin available 3 hours either side HW and suitable craft up to 25'LOA. Diesel from Harbour Commissioners' tank, petrol from garage in town, parking (c) on West Quay is often full (one trailer space): chandlery from Net Tec Marine Ltd, South Quay. No Charge but harbour dues payable.

Newquay (Newquay Bay)
Harbour Slip, South Quay Hill
From A 39 Bideford road take A 3059, or A 3058 from A 30 Penzance road; access is via Fore St. Granite slipway onto beach can be used at all states of tide but best 4 hours either side HW and suitable all craft up to 18'LOA. Diesel, car park (c), trailer park on South Quay (c), toilets (20 yds). Speed limit 4 knots in and out of harbour: powered boats are not allowed within 400m of the waterline of any Newquay beaches. Contact Harbour Master before launching Tel Newquay(0637) 872809. Charge. **Note:** slip and access must be kept clear at all times for lifeboat launching.

Hayle (St Ives Bay)
North Quay (Tekoa Hayle Ltd)
Follow A 3074 off A 30 Penzance road. Concrete slipway (ex lifeboat) onto shingle available for 3/4 hours either side HW. Fuel, parking for car and trailer, toilets nearby. Speed limit in harbour: contact Harbour Master for water-skiing. Charge.

St Ives (St Ives Bay)
Lifeboat Slipway, Wharf Road
Follow A 3074 off A 30 Penzance road; slipway is adjacent to the main road through the town. Concrete slip gives direct access to water for $2\frac{1}{2}$ hours either side HW or launch over the hard sandy beach at any time. Petrol from garage ($\frac{1}{2}$ mile), parking for car and trailer, toilets, chandlery. Speed limit 5mph around harbour in area clearly marked by buoys; outside this area there are no restrictions. Contact Harbour Master at Harbour Office on Smeatons Pier before launching Tel Penzance(0736) 795018. Short term moorings are available for boats which have launched and wish to remain in the harbour. Charge.

Penzance Harbour (Mounts Bay)
Albert Pier Slipway
From A 30: access is via Albert Pier or harbour car park. Concrete slipway available at all states of tide for small craft but not within $1\frac{1}{2}$ hours LWS for larger craft with outboards. Petrol from local garages, for diesel contact the Harbour Office, Wharf Road; trailers can be left in the trailer park by arrangement with the Harbour Office Tel Penzance(0736) 66113, toilets at Penzance SC (by arrangement) or at the station. Chandlery from Curnow Chandlers or Atlantic Aqua Sports. Speed limit 5mph; water-skiing allowed outside the harbour. Charge.

Marazion (Mounts Bay)

Turn off A 30 east of Penzance: site is close to causeway to St Michael's Mount. Concrete slipway onto shingle beach available at most states of tide. Fuel, parking for car and trailer (c) and toilets in village. Speed limit. Site is owned by Mounts Bay SC and is recommended for dinghies only. Charge.

Porthleven (Mounts Bay)
Quayside

Turn off A 394 at Helston, taking B 3304. Concrete slipway available for 3 hours either side HW suitable all craft. Fuel, parking for car and trailer, toilets, boat engineers and chandlers in village. Speed limit 3mph in inner harbour, 5mph in outer harbour. Apply to Harbour Master for permission to launch or advice Tel St Keverne(0326) 563042. Charge and harbour dues payable. **Note:** this can be a dangerous area in onshore winds.

Coverack
Harbour Slipway

Turn off A 394 at Helston, taking the A 3083 and B 3293/3294: site is on east side of Lizard peninsula. Concrete slipway onto firm sand available at all states of tide but best for 2/3 hours either side HW. Fuel in village, parking for car and trailer, toilets in village. Speed limit in harbour: water-skiing allowed offshore. Site gives access to sheltered waters in SW winds. Contact Harbour Master Tel St Keverne(0326) 280583. Charge.

Gillan Creek
St Anthony-in-Meneage (Sailaway St Anthony Ltd)

Follow A 3083 and B 3293 from Helston turning left and following signs to Manaccan until St Anthony is signed: site is on north side of creek. Ramp onto beach available for 3 hours either side HW suitable all craft up to 22'LOA: divers and jet skiers may not use this site. No fuel, parking for car and trailer (c), toilets, tractor, visitors' moorings, chandlery and boatyard facilities on site. Speed limit 6 knots in creek. Check for availability Tel Manaccan(032 623) 357. Charge.

Helford River
Gweek Quay Boatyard

Follow B 3291 from Falmouth to head of river; boatyard is in village. Concrete slipway available for 2 hours either side HW. Fuel, parking for car and trailer (c), toilets, chandlery from yard. Speed limit 6 knots: no water-skiing. Check for availability Tel Mawgan(032 622) 657. Charge.

Helford River
Port Navas YC

From A 394 Truro to Helston Rd, turn off in Mabe Burnthouse and follow signs to Mawnan Smith, then Constantine and Port Navas. Fairly steep concrete slipway available for 3 hours either side HW suitable dinghies and trailer-sailers. Fuel on site, toilets, chandlery from Falmouth Chandlers at Penryn, boatyard facilities from Gweek Boatyard. Speed limit 6 knots in river. Site is for use of club members: visitors must take out temporary membership. Further information Tel Falmouth(0326) 40419. Charge.

Helford River
Port Navas

Directions as above: site is in centre of village. Launching over hard shingle foreshore available 2/3 hours either side HW suitable for dinghies only. Speed limit 6 knots in river. Limited parking. No Charge.

Helford River
Helford Passage

From Falmouth follow minor roads to Mawnan Smith, then signs to Helford Passage. Shingle foreshore next to Ferry Boat Inn available for launching for 4 hours either side HW and suitable for dinghies only. No fuel, parking for car and trailer (c), toilets at pub. Speed limit 6 knots: no water-skiing. No Charge.

Falmouth Harbour

A large deep-water natural harbour which offers extensive sheltered waters for day-sailing. Vessels navigating within the harbour must do so at low speed and with due care and caution. There is a 5 knot speed limit in Penryn River, Restronguet Ck, St Just Ck, Percuil River and St Mawes Harbour and an 8 knot speed limit in Falmouth Inner Harbour. Water-skiing is permitted in designated areas; for further information contact the Harbour Office, 44 Arwenack St, Falmouth(0326) 312285/314379. In the port of Truro, water-skiing is only permitted in the designated area and a permit must first be obtained from the Harbour Master at the Harbour Office on the Town Quay Tel Truro(0872) 78131/72130.

Falmouth (Falmouth Harbour)
Grove Place Dinghy Park

Large slipway of brick and concrete blocks is available at all states of tide and suitable for all types of craft. Fuel from pontoon at Visitors' Yacht Haven, fuel barge or from local garages, parking for car and trailer adjacent (c), toilets, chandlery from M & P Miller, 15 Arwenack St. Charge.

Penryn (Falmouth Harbour)
Church Slip

Turn off A 39 towards Falmouth: Penryn is at head of river and site is just below the church on Flushing Rd. Shingle foreshore can be used for launching dinghies 2 hours either side HW. Fuel in town, limited parking for car and trailer, chandlers and boatyards in Penryn. No Charge.

Flushing (Falmouth Harbour)
Quayside

Follow signs off A 39 Falmouth to Truro road to Flushing. Concrete slipway available for 2 hours either side HW is suitable for dinghies only. Fuel in village, parking for car and trailer on quay (c). No Charge.

Flushing (Falmouth Harbour)
Trefusis Road

Follow signs to Flushing from A 39: access is via Trefusis Rd. Stone slipway onto shingle foreshore available for 3½ hours either side HW suitable dinghies only. No fuel, parking for car and trailer on Flushing Quay (200yds), toilets, nearest chandlers in Penryn. No Charge.

Mylor (Falmouth Harbour)
Mylor Yacht Harbour

Follow minor roads to south side Mylor Ck. Concrete slipway available at all states of tide. Fuel, parking for car and trailer (c), toilets and chandlery on site. Check for availability Tel Falmouth (0326) 72121. Charge.

Feock (Falmouth Harbour)
Loe Beach Boat Park

Turn off A 39 onto B 3289 and follow signs. Launch over shingle foreshore near HW. No fuel, parking for car and trailer (c), toilets. No Charge.

Truro (Falmouth Harbour)
Newham Quay Slip, Newham Road

Turn off A 39 Truro bypass into Newham Rd and turn left onto quay. Narrow concrete slipway with sharp bend at top and cill at half-tide available for 2 hours either side HW and is suitable for dinghies and other small craft. No fuel, limited parking. No Charge.

Truro (Falmouth Harbour)
Malpas Road
Turn left off A 39 Truro bypass at roundabout and follow signs to Malpas: site is adjacent Sharps Builders Merchants. Very narrow concrete slipway with cill well above half-tide mark available for 1½/2 hours either side HW and suitable dinghies only. Fuel from Truro, limited parking for car and trailer (c), chandlery from Penrose Outdoors, Truro. No Charge.

Truro (Falmouth Harbour)
Malpas Road, Sunny Corner
Turn left off A 39 Truro bypass at roundabout and follow signs to Malpas; site is opposite Truro Marina. Concrete slipway leads to muddy beach and is available for 2 hours either side HW. No fuel, limited parking, chandlery from Penrose Outdoors. No Charge.

Malpas (Falmouth Harbour)
Turn off A 39 Truro bypass at roundabout taking road to Malpas; site is below Heron Inn. Concrete slipway can be used for 2/3 hours either side HW but access is steep and narrow with sharp bends. No fuel, limited parking (c), toilets. No Charge

St Just in Roseland (Falmouth Harbour)
Pasco & Son
Follow B 3289 from Truro via King Harry Ferry; boatyard is adjacent church. Concrete slipway available at all states of tide. Diesel on site, parking for car and trailer (c) can be busy in season. Check for availability Tel St Mawes(0326) 270269. Charge

St Mawes (Falmouth Harbour)
Stone Quay, St Mawes SC
Follow A 3078 from A 39 east of Truro; site is ½ mile upstream from harbour and access is via a steep narrow lane with sharp bend. Concrete slipway onto sand/shingle foreshore is available at all states of tide for craft up to 16'LOA. No fuel, parking for car and trailer in village (c), toilets, chandlery from Percuil Boatyard. Temporary membership available Tel St Mawes(0326) 270686. Speed limit 5 knots in harbour. Charge

St Mawes (Falmouth Harbour)
Harbour Slipway
Follow A 3078 from A 39 east of Truro: site is outside the Ship and Castle Hotel and access is via narrow and often congested streets which make manoeuvring difficult. Steep concrete slipway available for 2 hours either side HW for larger craft or at all times for dinghies if cars can reverse onto beach. Petrol (1 mile), parking for car and trailer (c), toilets, chandlery and yard facilities from Percuil Boatyard. Speed limit 5 knots in harbour. See Harbour Master before launching Tel St Mawes(0326) 270553. Charge.

St Mawes (Falmouth Harbour)
Polvarth Boatyard (Hamling & Hitchings)
Follow A 3078 from A 39 east of Truro: site is at end of Polvarth Lane and upstream of Polvarth Pt and access is via a steep and narrow lane. Concrete slipway available for 4 hours either side HW during working hours only and suitable for craft up to 20'LOA. Fuel, parking for car and trailer (c), chandlery from Percuil Boatyard. Check for availability Tel St Mawes(0326) 270481. Charge.

Percuil (Falmouth Harbour)
Slipway
Turn off A 39 east of Truro onto A 3078 then follow minor roads: site is on east bank of Percuil River. Steep concrete slipway onto shingle beach available at all states of tide but suitable dinghies and powerboats only. No fuel, parking for car and trailer, toilets, boatyard facilities and chandlery from Percuil Boatyard. No Charge.

Place (Falmouth Harbour)
Place Manor
Turn off A 39 east of Truro taking A 3078 and turning off to Gerrans then follow signs:
site is opposite St Mawes just upstream of Amsterdam Pt. Concrete slipway available for
4 hours either side HW suitable dinghies only. No fuel, parking for car and trailer, boat
park. No Charge.

Portscatho
Harbour Slip
Turn off A 3078 to St Mawes and follow signs. Steep concrete and stone slipway onto
sand available at all states of tide and suitable for craft up to 16'LOA. Petrol, parking for
car and trailer (c), toilets and limited chandlery from Percuil Boatyard; repairs from John
Billing (Harbour Master). Speed limit 5mph within harbour and near beach but water-
skiing is permitted outside these areas. Contact Harbour Master Tel Portscatho(087 258)
616. Charge and harbour dues payable.

Fowey Harbour
**A deep-water harbour with good launching facilities and extensive sheltered
waters. There is a speed limit of 6 knots throughout the harbour and water-
skiing is not allowed. For further information contact Fowey Harbour Master
on Albert Quay Tel Fowey(072 683) 2471/2472.**

Caffa Mill Slip (Fowey Harbour)
From Lostwithiel, follow A 390/B 3269 and turn off following signs to Bodinnick Ferry.
Concrete slipway onto shingle available at all states of tide and suitable all craft. No
fuel, parking for car and trailer, dinghy storage, toilets and chandlers. For availability Tel
St Austell(0726) 74466. Overspill car park 200yds to north but parking and access
crowded at peak times. Charge

Golant Quay Slip (Fowey Harbour)
From Lostwithiel, follow A 390/B 3269 and turn off following signs to Golant; site is 2
miles north of Fowey. Concrete slipway available 3 hours either side HW. No fuel,
parking very restricted, toilets in village. For availability Tel Golant Quay Users
Fowey(072 683) 2314. This site can be very congested in summer. No Charge.

Penmarlam Slip, Yeate Farm (Fowey Harbour)
Follow A 38 west from Liskeard, taking A 390 at Dobwalls, then left onto B 3359 at E
Taphouse and left at next crossroads. After 5 miles, turn right towards Bodinnick: after
another 5 miles turn right into Yeate Farm. Concrete slipway onto hard beach available
at most states of tide and suitable for all craft although access to site is steep and
narrow. No fuel, parking for car and trailer (c), tractor and hoist available, boat storage
and camp site. Further information Tel Polruan(072 687) 256. Charge.

Polruan Quay Slip (Fowey Harbour)
Follow minor roads from Lostwithiel to Polruan. Concrete slipway available at all states
of tide. Fuel on quay, no parking, toilets and chandlers in Polruan. This is a small village
with steep narrow streets and suitable only for launching small craft by local
holidaymakers. For availability Tel Polruan(072 687) 260. Charge.

West Looe
Millpool Boatyard (Norman Pearn & Co Ltd)
From Plymouth follow A 38/A 374/A 387 and cross over bridge into West Looe: site is
100yds upstream. Concrete slipway available 4 hours either side HW during summer
months only. Fuel, parking for car and trailer (c), toilets and chandlery, crane and winch
available. Speed limit 5 knots; no water-skiing. Site is above bridge so not suitable for
boats with masts. Check for availability Tel Looe(050 36) 2244. Charge.

Millendreath
Millendreath Holiday Village
Follow A 374/387 west from Torpoint, taking B 3253 at Widegates and following signs. Tractor launching for dinghies and powerboats. Fuel, parking for car and trailer (c), toilets, chandlery from Looe Chandlers, boatyard facilities from Norman Pearn, Looe: full watersport facilities, shop and café. Further information Tel Looe(050 36) 3281. Charge.

Downderry
Downderry Slipway
From Plymouth follow A 38/A 374/A 387/B 3247; site is 3 miles east of Looe. Concrete slip available for 2/3 hours either side HW or at all states of tide for dinghies. No fuel, no parking or space for trailers, toilets. No water-skiing. No Charge.

Portwrinkle
Harbour Slip
From Plymouth, follow A 38/A 374/A 387/B 3247. Concrete slipway available at all states of tide or for larger craft at HW. Lockable bollards limit the size of boat which can be launched: the key is held by the Harbour Master who lives nearby. No fuel, parking for car and trailer, toilets. No water-skiing. No Charge.

Plymouth Harbour
A large deep-water harbour which is a busy naval and commercial port. All small craft must keep clear of large ships: there is a speed limit of 10 knots and water-skiing is not allowed within the harbour which is under the jurisdiction of the Queen's Harbour Master, Longroom, Stonehouse Tel Plymouth(0752) 663225 ext 2411/2. Water-skiing is permitted in Plymouth Sound and in restricted areas in Rivers Plym and Tamar.

Landrake (Plymouth Harbour)
Follow A 38 from Saltash to Landrake turning left when signposted "Boating World" and following signs for 2 miles. Launching for small craft available 3 hours either side HW: travel hoist and marine services available for larger craft. Site gives access to Rivers Lynher, Tamar and St Germans. Further information Tel Landrake(075 538) 679. Charge.

Millbrook, Torpoint (Plymouth Harbour)
Southdown Quay (Seaward Marine Enterprises)
From Plymouth, take A 374 via Torpoint ferry then B 3247 to Millbrook. Shingle hard available for 2½ hours either side HW suitable all craft up to 20'LOA. Fuel nearby, parking for car and trailer in security area (c), toilets and showers, chandlers. Other facilities available Tel Plymouth(0752) 823084. Charge.

Torpoint (Plymouth Harbour)
The Ballast Pound Yacht Harbour Ltd.
From Plymouth take A 374 via Torpoint ferry: site is signposted by Ballast Pound. Shingle foreshore can be used for launching at all times except for 2/3 hours at LWS. Do not use adjacent concrete slip which belongs to SC. Fuel in Torpoint, arrangement can be made to leave vehicles in pub car park (½ mile) (c), toilets (¼ mile). Launching by prior arrangement only Tel Plymouth(0752) 813658. Charge.

Saltash (River Tamar)
Jubilee Green and Waterside
From Plymouth follow A 38 to Saltash. Concrete slipway available at all states of tide. No fuel, parking but not for trailers, toilets, chandlery from Plymouth. No Charge.

Cargreen (River Tamar)
Old Ferry Slip
Turn off A 388 Saltash to Callington road following signs: site is opposite the Spaniard Inn. Concrete slipway available approx 2 hours either side HW and suitable all craft up to 20'LOA. No fuel, parking for car and trailer, toilets, pub facilities. Speed limit. No Charge.

Calstock (River Tamer)
4 Follow signs from A 390 Liskeard to Tavistock road: access is via narrow roads only.
Steep concrete slipway available for 2/3 hours either side HW and suitable all craft up to
20'LOA. Fuel (5 miles), parking (often congested) for car and trailer (c), telephone and
toilets: yard facilities including crane and winch available at Calstock Boatyard. Speed
limit. No Charge.

DEVON

Plymouth (Plymouth Harbour)
Mayfower International Marina, Richmond Walk
Follow signs from city centre. Steel dock with crane is available at all times for launching.
Fuel from marina, parking for car and trailer (c), toilets, showers and chandlers and many
other facilities. Boats are craned into the water and can be berthed in marina when not
in use. Further information Tel Plymouth(0752) 556633. Charge.

Plymouth (Plymouth Harbour)
Sutton Harbour
Sutton Harbour is located to the east of Plymouth Hoe near the Barbican: site is on east
side of harbour. Concrete slipway available for 4 hours either side HW. Fuel, parking
difficult (c), toilets, chandlers nearby. Charge

Coxside (Plymouth Harbour)
Queen Anne's Battery Marina
Coxside is signposted on entering the city from the east. Concrete slipway available at
all states of tide. Fuel, parking for car and trailer (c), toilets and showers, chandlery and
all marina facilities. Further information Tel Plymouth(0752) 671142. Charge.

Newton Ferrers (Newton Creek, River Yealm)
Bridgend Quay
Turn off A 379 Kingsbridge to Plymouth road and follow B 3186; site is at head of creek.
Concrete slipway available for $2\frac{1}{2}$ hours either side HW. No fuel, limited parking, no
toilets, chandlery from Yealm Boat Co. Speed limit 6 knots: no water-skiing. Site gives
access to deep, sheltered waters. No Charge.

Bantham (River Avon)
Follow A 379 from Kingsbridge, turning left to Thurlestone Sands and thence to Bantham.
Concrete slipway available for 2 hours either side HW. No fuel, parking for car and
trailer nearby (c). Speed limit: no water-skiing. Apply Bantham Harbour Master or
Bantham SC. There are strong tidal currents in the river entrance. No Charge.

Salcombe Harbour
**Nearly 2,000 acres of tidal waters lie between the entrance to the harbour,
"The Bar" and Kingsbridge and these provide an excellent sheltered area for
day-sailing. The Harbour Office is on Whitestrand Tel Salcombe (054 884)
3791 but during peak summer months, launches marked "Harbour Master"
patrol the Estuary between 0600 and 2200. All craft must pay harbour dues
and display a licence disc which can be obtained from the Harbour Office, Car
and Boat Park Attendant or South Sands Attendant. There is a speed limit of 8
knots and water-skiing is prohibited in the harbour.**

South Sands (Salcombe Harbour)
Follow coast road 1 mile south from town centre. Short concrete slipway onto firm sand
on south side of beach available at all states of tide and suitable small craft up to
18'LOA. No fuel, parking for car and trailer on beach (c), toilets at North Sands ($\frac{1}{2}$ mile),
chandlers in Salcombe. Speed limit 8 knots. No Charge but harbour dues payable.

Salcombe (Salcombe Harbour)
Whitestrand Quay
Site is in town centre. Concrete slipway onto shingle available for 3 hours either side HW or up to 1 hour either side of LW over shingle. Fuel from fuel barge or town, parking for car (c) short stay but trailer cannot be left, toilets, chandlery from Salcombe Chandlers. Site only suitable for dinghies and other light craft. No Charge but harbour dues payable.

Salcombe (Salcombe Harbour)
Shadycombe Car Park
Site is in town centre. Concrete slipway available for 3 hours either side HW for larger craft or at all states of tide over shingle for small craft. Fuel in town, parking for car and trailer (c) adjacent, boat park, chandlers in town. No Charge but harbour dues payable.

Salcombe (Salcombe Harbour)
Batson Slip
Site is to north of town, near main car park. Large concrete slipway onto shingle foreshore available at all states of tide. Fuel from town or fuel barge, parking for car, boat and trailer (c), toilets, chandlery from Winters Marine. An attendant is on duty 0900-1800 every day during the season, when it may be advisable to reserve car/boat parking spaces. No Charge but harbour dues payable.

Kingsbridge (Salcombe Harbour)
Squares Slip
Follow A 381 from Totnes or A 379 from Plymouth. Site is at Squares Quay at head of estuary and adjacent car park. Concrete slipway available for 2½ hours either side HW for dinghies: larger craft (up to 5' draught) can be launched at HW. Fuel from nearby garage, parking for car (c), trailers can be left by arrangement, toilets. No Charge but harbour dues payable.

Dartmouth Harbour and River Dart
The River Dart forms an attractive natural harbour, with sheltered waters for day-sailing which are navigable as far as the bridge at Totnes. There is a speed limit of 6 knots throughout the harbour with Dead Slow speed requested in Home Reach, Totnes and water-skiing is not permitted. The Harbour Office is at the Old Post Office, South Embankment Tel Dartmouth(080 43) 2337. Harbour dues are payable.

Dartmouth (River Dart)
Higher Ferry Slip (South Side)
From town centre follow signs to Higher Ferry. Concrete slipway is available at all states of tide. Fuel from town, parking for car and trailer nearby (c), toilets nearby. The ferry operates from the north side of this slip and must not be obstructed. No Charge but harbour dues payable.

Dartmouth (River Dart)
Dart Marina, Sandquay
From town centre follow signs to Higher Ferry. Two concrete slipways available at all states of tide. Fuel, parking for car and trailer, toilets and chandlery on site: shower and changing facilities at Dart Marina Hotel. Check for availability Tel Dartmouth(080 43) 3351. Charge.

Dittisham (River Dart)
Ham Car Park
Follow signs from Dartmouth: access is through car park. Shingle foreshore available at all states of tide suitable for launching small craft only. No fuel, ample parking and toilets. No Charge but harbour dues payable.

Totnes (River Dart)
Ashford Slip, Mill Tail (off The Plains)
Follow A 38 from Exeter/Plymouth turning off onto A 385. Concrete slipway available for 3 hours either side HW. Fuel in town, very limited parking, toilets nearby, chandlery from Compass Sailing & Boating, 71 High Street. Charge and harbour dues payable.

Totnes (River Dart)
Follow A 38 from Exeter turning off onto A 385. Site is near Totnes Rowing Club, ¼ mile downstream from the lower road bridge; follow signs for Motor Museum. Concrete slipway available at most states of tide except LWS. Fuel in town, parking for car and trailer (c), toilets nearby, chandlery from Compass Sailing & Boating. Charge and harbour dues payable.

Stoke Gabriel (River Dart)
Follow signs from A 385 Totnes road. Concrete slipway onto shingle available for 3 hours either side HW suitable small craft only. Fuel in village, limited parking (c), toilets. Charge and harbour dues payable.

Galmpton Creek (River Dart)
Dartside Boatyard
Turn off Torbay ring road B 3022: site is 3 miles upriver. Concrete slipway available for 2/3 hours either side HW. Fuel from Dartmouth, parking for car and trailer (c), chandlery. Check for availability Tel Churston(0803) 842269/843627. Charge and harbour dues payable.

Greenway Quay (River Dart)
Follow A 3022 from Paignton, turning right at Galmpton: site is opposite Dittisham. Concrete slipway available at all states of tide. No fuel, limited parking (c). Check for availability Tel Churston(0803) 844010. Charge (pay ferryman) and harbour dues payable.

Kingswear (River Dart)
Follow A 379 from Torquay; site is opposite Dartmouth and close south of River Dart YC. This is a dead-end with very confined turning space for cars and trailers. Cobbled slipway available for 4 hours either side HW and suitable craft up to 16'LOA. Fuel, parking for car and trailer (c), toilets, chandlery from Kingswear Marina adjacent. Charge.

Brixham Harbour
Breakwater Slipway
From Exeter follow A 38/A 380/A 3022 to Brixham Harbour. Concrete slipway available at all states of tide. Fuel from local garages, limited parking on Breakwater Hard; trailer can be left (c), toilets, chandlery from Portbury Marine. Speed limit 5 knots in harbour; no water-skiing. This is primarily a fishing port and pleasure boating is not given top priority. Charge.

Brixham Harbour
Freshwater Quarry
From Exeter follow A 38/A 380/A 3022 to Brixham Harbour. Concrete slipway available at all states of tide. Fuel from local garages, parking for car and trailer (c), chandlery from Portbury Marine. Charge.

Paignton Harbour
Harbour Slip
From Exeter follow A 38/A 380/A 3022 to Paignton. Concrete slipway onto hard sand available for 5 hours either side HW suitable all craft up to 25'LOA. Fuel (150yds), parking for car and trailer (c) nearby, toilets, chandlery from Queen Anne Marine, Beacon Quay, Torquay. Speed limit 5 knots in harbour and inshore: water-skiing permitted in designated areas. A small busy harbour which welcomes visitors· moorings and quay berths for boats up to 21'LOA are available for short term stays from the Harbour Master Tel Torquay(0803) 22429. Charge and harbour dues payable.

Torquay Harbour
Beacon Quay
From Exeter follow A 38/A 380 to Torquay seafront. Three concrete slipways with wooden ends are available at all states of tide except within 1 hour LW and suitable all craft up to 25'LOA. Fuel from fuelling jetty nearby, parking for car (c), trailer park (c) within 1 mile, toilets nearby, chandlery from Queen Anne Marine, crane. Speed limit 5 knots in harbour and within beach markers: water-skiing permitted in designated areas. Contact Harbour Master Tel Torquay(0803) 22429. Torquay Marina adjacent has moorings and all facilities. Charge and harbour dues payable.

Babbacombe
Babbacombe Beach
Follow A 379 from Exeter and B 3199 turning off to beach. Steep, narrow road to car park with locked barrier giving access to concrete slipway onto sandy but rocky beach suitable small craft only. Obtain key and advice from Beach Master on site. Fuel in town, parking for car and trailer (c), toilets. Charge.

Teignmouth (River Teign)
Shaldon
Follow A 379 north from Torquay and turn into Fore St then take first left turn into Albion St with slipway at far end. Concrete slipway onto shingle available for 4 hours either side HW suitable craft up to 20'LOA. Fuel, parking for car and trailer (c), toilets, chandlery from Brigantine Yacht Chandlers on the quay. No Charge.

Combeinteignhead (River Teign)
Coombe Cellars
From Exeter follow A 379/B 3195 to south side of river, 2 miles from estuary mouth and above road bridge. Concrete slipway available for 3 hours either side HW. No fuel, parking for car and trailer, toilets in Coombe Cellars Inn nearby. For water-skiing contact South Devon Water Sports Club. No Charge.

Teignmouth (River Teign)
Polly Steps Car Park
From Exeter follow A 379: access is via Quay St and site is on west side of docks. Concrete slipway available at all states of tide. No fuel, parking for car and trailer, chandlery from Brigantine Yacht Chandlers in Shaldon. Speed limit 10 mph: no water-skiing in river. This is the best site in Teignmouth. No Charge.

Teignmouth (River Teign)
Gales Hill Slipway
From Exeter follow A 379/A 381: site is next to quay. Shingle hard available at all states of tide. Fuel (100 yds), parking in car park (200 yds); no trailers, toilets in car park, chandlery from Brigantine Yacht Chandlers in Shaldon. Speed limit 10 knots: no water-skiing in river. No Charge.

Exmouth
Exmouth is situated on the east side of the Exe Estuary and the entrance to the river where there is a bar, can be dangerous in strong onshore winds, especially with the wind against tide. At half ebb the tide runs very strongly through the narrow river entrance. There are six miles of navigable channel in the estuary. Speed limit 10 knots in river: water-skiing allowed in designated areas.

Trinity Buoy Store (Exmouth)
Leave M 5 at junction 30 following A 376: approach via the Docks Relief Rd. Launching from shingle hard available for 2 hours either side HW suitable small craft only. Fuel, parking for car and trailer, chandlers and boatyards in town. No Charge.

Imperial Recreation Ground (Exmouth)
Leave M 5 at junction 30 following A 376: access is via Royal Avenue. Concrete slipway available for 3 hours either side of HW and suitable all craft. Fuel, parking for car and trailer, toilets, chandlers and boatyards in town. No Charge.

Mamhead Slipway (Exmouth)
Leave M 5 at junction 30, following A 376: site is at west end of Esplanade near pier. Steep concrete slipway with steel ramp onto sandy beach available at all states of tide. Fuel from local garages, parking for car and trailer and toilets nearby, chandlers in town. No Charge.

Shelley Road (Exmouth)
Leave M 5 at junction 30 following A 376: site has narrow access from Docks Relief Rd. Launching over shingle for 3 hours either side HW suitable small craft only. Fuel, parking for car and trailer, chandlers and boatyards in town. No Charge.

Carlton Slipway (Exmouth)
Leave M 5 at junction 30 following A 376: access to beach from Esplanade. Launching across shingle beach for small craft which can be manhandled. No fuel, parking for car and trailer, toilets, chandlers and boatyards in town. No Charge.

Lifeboat Slipway (Exmouth)
Leave M 5 at junction 30 following A 376: access via Queen's Drive. Launching across shingle beach for small craft which can be manhandled. No fuel, parking for car and trailer, toilets, chandlers and boatyards in town. No Charge.

Lympstone (River Exe)
Sowden End
Leave M 5 at junction 30 taking A 376 and turning off into Lympstone: access to site is via Sowden Lane. Stone slipway available for 3 hours either side HW and suitable small craft and windsurfers only. No facilities. No Charge.

Axmouth (River Axe)
Seaton Marine Services
Turn off A 30 at Chard onto A 358 and B 3172: site is on west side of river. Concrete slipway available for launching at most times but gives access to sea for only 2½ hours either side HW. Fuel, parking for car and trailer, toilets, chandlery, moorings and boatyard facilities. Speed limit 8 knots inshore; water-skiing allowed outside limits. Check for availability Tel Seaton(0297) 23344. Charge.

DORSET

Lyme Regis
The Cobb
Follow A 35 west from Dorchester and A 3052 to Lyme Regis: access to harbour is via a steep hill (Cobb Rd). Temporary wood and steel slipway available at all states of tide for craft which can be manhandled or for 3 hours either side HW for larger craft (up to 1 ton). Fuel, parking for car (c) and trailer (in trailer park(c)): site is very congested in summer. Speed limit 2 knots in harbour: water-skiing allowed west of harbour and offshore. No swimming or Jet Ski boats allowed in harbour. All boats launched must be out of the harbour by the end of the day. Charge.

West Bay, Bridport
East Basin
Follow B 3157 from A 35. Concrete slipway onto wood available for 3 hours either side HW. Fuel (50yds), car parking adjacent (c), trailer park either side of slipway, toilets, chandlery from Lyme Bay Marine. Speed limit 8 knots: water-skiing offshore. Charge.

Weymouth
Commercial Road Quay

From Esplanade roundabout at clock tower, turn right into King St, then left at the bottom, turning into Commercial Rd at the next roundabout: site is opposite multi-storey carpark. Concrete slipway available at all states of tide for shallow draught craft: craft with deep draught should check with the Harbour Office before launching and suitable all craft up to 20/22'LOA. Fuel parking for car and trailer (c), winch, toilets and telephone: chandlery and yard facilities available in town. Craft should proceed at dead slow speed in the harbour. Details of designated water-skiing areas can be obtained from the Harbour Office, 20 Custom House Quay Tel Weymouth(0305) 206421. Charge (harbour dues payable if craft stays overnight).

Peveril Point, Swanage
Peveril Boat Park

Follow signs from Swanage High St. Concrete slipway available at all states of tide. No fuel, limited parking, toilets nearby. Charge.

27

South Coast: Studland to North Foreland

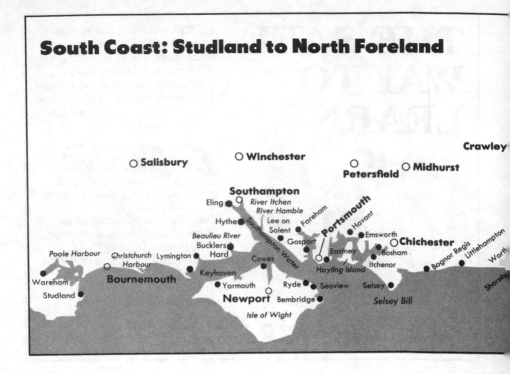

DORSET
Studland
Shell Bay Cafe, Shell Bay
Leave Poole on A 351 to Swanage, turning off to Studland on B 3351: access to site is via toll road to Sandbanks ferry. Concrete slipway available for 4 hours either side HW. No fuel, limited parking for car and trailer (c), toilets. Speed limit within yellow marker buoys: water-skiing allowed offshore. Check for availability Tel Studland(092 944) 363. Charge.

Poole Harbour
The second largest natural harbour in the world, Poole offers a large area of sheltered water, especially for shallow-draught boats. It is a busy commercial port, ferry port and popular yachting centre: take care not to obstruct the passage of vessels which cannot manoeuvre because of their draught. There is a chain ferry across the entrance and there is a double HW at the entrance, except at neaps. There is no speed limit in the harbour and water-skiing is allowed in specified areas: further information can be obtained from the Harbour Office on the Town Quay, Tel Poole(0202) 685261. All vessels over 14'LOA or with a 5 HP+ engine are liable to harbour dues.

Wareham (River Frome)
Ridge Wharf Yacht Centre
Follow A 351 Swanage road, turning left in Stoborough and passing through Ridge village: site is on the south bank of the river, 1 mile below Wareham. Concrete slipway with large winch available at all states of tide, except within 1 hour LW. Fuel, parking for car and trailer (c), toilets and chandlery on site. Speed limit 4 knots in river: water-skiing allowed in Wareham Ck. Check for availability Tel Wareham(092 95) 2650. Charge.

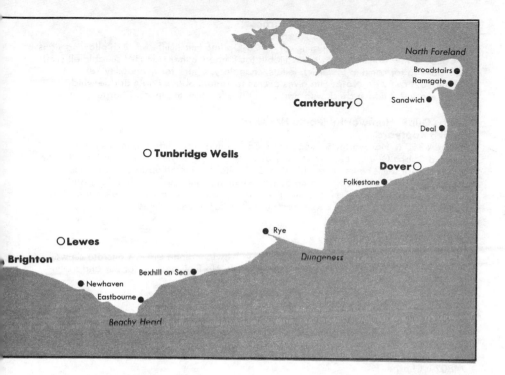

Wareham (River Frome)
Redcliffe Farm
Follow A 351 to Wareham turning off in Stoborough and following signs. Concrete slipway into River Frome available for ½ hour either side HW and suitable all craft. Fuel, parking for car and trailer (c), toilets. Speed limit of 4 knots in river; water skiing allowed in Wareham Ck. Site is 1½ miles from open water of Poole Harbour. Check for availability Tel Wareham(092 95) 51112. Charge

Rockley Sands, Hamworthy (Poole Harbour)
Rockley Boating Services
Follow A 350 to Hamworthy, turning off to follow signs to Rockley Pt. Shingle hard available 4 hours either side HW. No fuel, parking for car and trailer (c), toilets, storage facilities. Check for availability Tel Poole(0202) 674892. Charge.

Lake Drive, Hamworthy (Poole Harbour)
Dorset Lake Shipyard (Dorset Yacht Co)
Follow A 350 to Hamworthy, turning right into Lake Rd and thence to Lake Drive: larger boats can take route via Ashmore Ave, Lulworth Ave and thence Lake Drive. Concrete slipway available at all states of tide except for 1 hour either side LWS and suitable all craft up to 20'LOA. Fuel, limited parking for car and trailer, crane, toilets, chandlery and boatyard facilities on site. Check for availability (during working hours only) Tel Poole(0202) 674531/3. Charge.

Cobbs Quay, Hamworthy (Poole Harbour)
Cobbs Quay Ltd, Woodlands Avenue
Follow A 350 to Hamworthy, turning off by Co-Op into Hinchcliffe Rd and following signs
to Cobbs Quay. Concrete slipway available for 3 hours either side HW suitable all craft.
Fuel, parking for car and trailer (c), toilets, chandlery. Check for availability Tel
Poole(0202) 674299. **Note:** Site gives access to waters above Poole Bridge which
opens every 2/3 hours: check with Harbour Office for opening times. Charge.

Cobbs Quay, Hamworthy (Poole Harbour)
Davis's Boatyard
Follow A 350 to Hamworthy turning left by Co-Op into Hinchcliffe Rd, then Woodlands
Ave and Cobbs Quay. Concrete slipway available during daylight hours and at all states
of tide except for 2 hours either side LWS and suitable all craft up to 24'LOA. Fuel,
parking for car and trailer (c), crane by arrangement, winch, toilets, chandlery and
boatyard facilities on site. **Note:** site gives access to waters above Poole Bridge which
opens every 2/3 hours: check with Harbour Office for opening times. Charge.

Poole (Poole Harbour)
Baiter Public Slipway
Follow signs from the Town Quay: access is via Newfoundland Drive. Concrete slipway
available at all states of tide and suitable all craft. No fuel, parking for car and trailer
(c), toilets, chandlers in town. Charge.

Sandbanks (Poole Harbour)
Westons Point Boatyard, Turks Lane (Latham & Son)
Follow Sandbanks Rd from town centre, turning into Turks Lane after passing Whitecliff
recreation ground. Concrete slipway available for 4 hours either side HW. Fuel ($\frac{1}{2}$ mile),
no parking or toilets but chandlery on site. Check for availability Tel Parkstone(0202)
748029. Charge.

Sandbanks (Poole Harbour)
Mitchells Boatyard, Turks Lane
Follow Sandbanks Rd from town centre, turning into Turks Lane after passing Whitecliff
recreation ground. Concrete slipway available for 4 hours either side HW suitable all
craft. Fuel ($\frac{1}{2}$ mile), parking for car and trailer (c), crane, toilets, chandlery from Vintage
Boat Co on site, boatyard facilities. Check for availability Tel Parkstone(0202) 747857.
Charge.

Lilliput (Poole Harbour)
Salterns Boatyard, 38 Salterns Way
Turn off Sandbanks Rd into Salterns Way. Slipway, two boat hoists for craft up to 27'LOA
and 5 tons and a travel hoist for launching boats up to 65'LOA and 40 tons available
during working hours. All facilities on site. Check for availability Tel Poole(0202) 707321.
Charge.

Sandbanks (Poole Harbour)
Royston Pizey & Co Ltd, 324 Sandbanks Road (Lilliput Yacht Station)
Follow Sandbanks Rd from town centre. Concrete slipway available for 3 hours either
side HW and suitable all craft up to 28'LOA and max draught 3'9''. Fuel, parking for car
and trailer (c), toilets, chandlery and boatyard facilities on site. Check for availability Tel
Canford Cliffs(0202) 707176. Charge.

Sandbanks (Poole Harbour)
Sandbanks Yacht Co Ltd, 32 Panorama Road
Follow signs to Sandbanks from town centre. Concrete slipway available during daylight
hours at all states of tide except 1$\frac{1}{2}$ hours either side LWS and suitable all craft up to
20'LOA. Fuel, parking for car and trailer(c), toilets, chandlery and boatyard facilities on
site. Check for availability Tel Canford Cliffs(0202) 707500. Charge.

Sandbanks (Poole Harbour)
Davis's Grasmere Boatyard
Follow signs to Sandbanks: site is at end of Sandy Lane off Panorama Rd. Launching over sandy foreshore available at all times but suitable small craft only. No fuel, very limited parking. Check for availability Tel Canford Cliffs(0202) 708068. Charge.

Christchurch Harbour
Much of this attractive harbour dries at LW. A double HW leads to a stand of 3-4 hours and currents in the harbour entrance are strong, especially in The Run. Water-skiing is not allowed inside the harbour where there is a 5 knot speed limit. Further information from the Quay and Moorings Superintendent whose office is on Mudeford Quay Tel Highcliffe (042 52) 4933.

Southbourne (River Stour)
Wick Lane
Follow B 3059 from Bournemouth, turning right into Wick Lane before bridge: site is on south bank, downstream of Tuckton Bridge. Concrete slipway available for 2/3 hours either side HW. Fuel from garage nearby, parking for car and trailer, toilets. No Charge.

Christchurch (River Stour)
Quomps, Mayors Mead Car Park
Approach through car park at west end of town: site is adjacent to Pontin's Holiday Camp. Wide concrete slipway available at all states of tide. No fuel, parking for car (c) and trailer, toilets (100yds), chandlery from Slaters Marine, Barrack Rd. No Charge.

Christchurch (River Avon)
Rossiter Yachts, Bridge Street
Turn off B 3059: site is south of Bridge St on west bank of east arm of river. Concrete slipway available by arrangement only. Fuel from nearby garage, parking for car and trailer, chandlery. Check for availability Tel Christchurch(0202) 483250. Crane for mast-stepping available. Charge.

Christchurch (River Avon)
Bridge Street
Turn off B 3059: site is on east bank of east arm of river, just south of the road and adjacent to the car park in front of the Civic Offices. Concrete slipway available for approx 4 hours either side HW and suitable small craft only. Fuel, parking for car and trailer (c), toilets, telephone, chandlery from South West Marine nearby. No Charge.

Christchurch Harbour
Argyle Road, Fisherman's Bank
Turn off B 3059 east of town following signs to Stanpit: Argyle Rd is off Stanpit, past Stanpit Garage and opposite the Recreation Ground. Argyle Rd is a cul-de-sac and turning and manoeuvring space is very restricted. Launching from tarmac and shingle foreshore for 2 hours either side HW suitable small craft which can be manhandled. Petrol from Stanpit Garage, limited parking in nearby streets, toilets, nearest chandlers Roy Stride, Coastguard Way. No Charge.

Mudeford
Mudeford Quay
From town centre follow signs to Mudeford: access is through car park on Quay. Concrete slipway onto hard foreshore available for 4 hours either side HW. Fuel from garage (½ mile), parking for car (c) and trailer, toilets, cafe and pub on site: nearest chandlers Roy Stride, Coastguard Way. Car park is very busy in summer. No Charge.

HAMPSHIRE

Keyhaven
The Quay Slipway
Follow A 337 from Lymington or New Milton, following signs to Milford-on-Sea and Keyhaven: after passing the Gun Inn, turn left towards Keyhaven YC and entrance to Quay will be seen ahead. Concrete slipway onto shingle available for 3 hours either side HW and suitable craft up to 20' LOA. No fuel, parking for car (c) and trailer, toilets, chandlery from Milford Chandlers (1 mile), boatyard facilities from West Solent Boatbuilders (closed at weekends). Speed limit 6 knots in river and within 300yds of shore: site can be very congested at peak times. Charge.

Lymington (Lymington River)
Harbour Commissioner's Slip, Town Quay
Leave M 27 at junction 1 and follow A 337 to Lymington: site is on Town Quay opposite chandlers "Shipmates". Concrete slipway onto gravel available at all states of tide. Fuel, parking for car and trailer (c), toilets and chandlers. Speed limit 6 knots in river; no water-skiing or windsurfing. Charge.

Lymington (Lymington River)
Harbour Commissioner's Slip, Bath Road
Leave M 27 at junction 1 following A 337 to town centre and turning right at the bottom of the High Street: site is past Lymington Marina. Concrete slipway onto shingle available at all states of tide except for 1 hour either side LWS. Fuel from marina adjacent, parking for car and trailer (c), toilets, chandlers. Speed limit 6 knots in river: no water-skiing or windsurfing. Take great care when ferries are approaching. Charge.

Beaulieu River
Bucklers Hard Yacht Harbour
Leave M 27 at junction 1 following A 337, turning onto B 3056 at Lyndhurst; take third turning to the left on the road from Beaulieu and report to Harbour Master's Office. Concrete slipway available for 5 hours either side HW suitable sailing craft. Fuel, parking for car and trailer (c), toilets, chandlers, boatyard all on site. Site gives access to sheltered water and village has facilities including a hotel, shop, garage and maritime museum. Speed limit 5 knots: no water-skiing. Further information Tel Bucklers Hard(059 063) 200/234. Charge.

ISLE OF WIGHT

Yarmouth
South Quay
From Cowes follow A 3020 and A 3054 west. Two concrete slipways into the harbour and one wooden slipway above the bridge into the river suitable for launching by hand only: all available at all states of tide. Fuel, parking for car and trailer in nearby car park (c), toilets on quay, chandlery from Harwoods in St James's Square. Speed limit 4 knots: no water-skiing. Further information from the Harbour Master Tel Yarmouth (0983) 760300. Keep clear of ferries entering and leaving the harbour at all times. No Charge.

Gurnard
Shore Road
Follow signs from A 3020 and B 3325 to Gurnard: site is adjacent sailing club. Concrete slipway available for 3 hours either side HW. No fuel, limited parking, trailers can be left by slip, toilets, chandlers in Cowes. Site suitable small craft and windsurfers. No Charge.

34

Cowes Harbour

Probably the most prestigious yachting centre in the Country, Cowes is ideally situated for access to the Solent. The Medina River is navigable to Newport at HW. There is a speed limit of 6 knots and water-skiing is not allowed in the harbour. For further information contact the Harbour Master on the Old Town Quay Tel Cowes(0983) 293952. All slips are within easy reach of chandlers, fuel, boatyard facilities etc in the town.

Egypt Point Slip (West Cowes)

Site is at junction of Egypt Hill and the Esplanade. Concrete slipway available for 3 hours either side HW. No fuel, parking for car and trailer (c), toilets, chandlers. No Charge.

Watch House Slip (West Cowes)

Access is from the southern end of the Parade. Concrete slipway available for 4 hours either side HW and suitable most craft. No fuel, parking for car and trailer (c), toilets, chandlers. Site may be congested at peak times. No Charge.

Post Office Slip (West Cowes)

Site is adjacent to the Post Office and opposite Market Hill: access is from Bath Rd. Launching from tarmac onto shingle available for 3 hours either side HW. No fuel, nearest car park in Terminus Rd (c), toilets, chandlers. Suitable small craft which can be manhandled only. No Charge.

Sun Hill Slip (West Cowes)

Site is off High St, adjacent Midland Bank and opposite Sun Hill. Concrete and stone slipway onto shingle available for 3 hours either side HW and suitable small craft only as access is often congested. No fuel or parking: if locked, obtain key from Harbour Office, Town Quay. No Charge.

Town Quay Slip (West Cowes)

Site is adjacent to the Fountain Hotel and the Red Funnel Terminal in the High St. Concrete slipway available for 3 hours either side HW. Fuel, no parking, toilets, chandlers. Access is busy and vehicular approach difficult so site is suitable only for small craft. Harbour Office is adjacent. No Charge.

Medina Road (West Cowes)

Site is opposite Bridge Road. Concrete slipway onto shingle available for 4 hours either side HW and suitable small craft only. No fuel, no parking, toilets, chandlers. No Charge.

Dover Road (East Cowes)

Site is adjacent to the Red Funnel Terminal. Concrete slipway is available for 4 hours either side HW. Fuel, parking for car and trailer (c), chandlers in West Cowes. No Charge.

Albany Road (East Cowes)

Access via the Esplanade. Masonry slipway is only available at HW and suitable for small craft only. No fuel, parking for car and trailer, toilets, chandlers in West Cowes. No Charge.

Newport (River Medina)
Town Quay

Follow A 3020 from Cowes or A 3054 from Ryde: site is at the junction of Sea St with the Town Quay. Steep concrete slipway available for 1½ hours either side HW and suitable craft up to 20'LOA. Fuel, parking for car but not for trailer, hand operated crane, toilets (summer only), chandlery from Hunter & Coombes Ltd, repair facilities from Odessa Shipyard. Site is close to entrance of large transport yard so exercise caution during weekday periods and take care not to obstruct. Speed limit 4 knots. Contact Harbour Master for further information Tel Newport(0983) 525994. No Charge.

Newport (River Medina)
Seaclose Quay
Follow A 3020 from Cowes or A 3054 from Ryde: site is reached via the Town Quay and is adjacent British Road Services. Concrete slipway available for 1½ hours either side HW. No fuel, no parking, toilets (summer only), chandlery from Hunter & Coombes Ltd. Further information from the Harbour Master Tel Newport(0983) 525994. No Charge.

Island Harbour Marina, Mill Lane (River Medina)
Turn off A 3054 Newport to Ryde road into Fairlee Rd: site is on east bank of river downstream of Newport. Concrete slipway into locked basin available 4 hours either side HW and suitable all craft. Diesel, parking for car and trailer, toilets, telephone and yard facilities on site. Further information Tel Isle of Wight(0983) 526020. Charge.

Whippingham (River Medina)
The Folly Inn
Site is on east bank Medina River, upstream of East Cowes: access is via Folly Lane off the A 3054. Concrete slipway at end of hard available at all states of tide. No fuel, parking for car and trailer, toilets and showers (c), pub and restaurant facilities. Further information Tel Isle of Wight(0983) 297171. No Charge.

Ryde
St Thomas' Street
Concrete slipway onto beach west of Pier available for 3 hours either side HW. No fuel, parking for car (c) but not for trailer, toilets. Speed limit 6 knots inshore. No Charge.

Ryde
Quay Road
Site is adjacent to the Hovercraft Terminus east of Pier. Slipway of stone setts onto beach is available for 3 hours either side HW. No fuel, parking for car and trailer (c), toilets, no chandlers. Speed limit 6 knots inshore. No Charge.

Ryde
Eastern Gardens
Site is at west end of gardens and east of Pier: access is via the Esplanade. Concrete slipway onto beach available for 3 hours either side HW. No fuel, parking for car (c) but not for trailer, toilets. Speed limit 6 knots inshore. No Charge.

Ryde
Northwalk
Site is opposite the canoe lake and east of Pier. Iron slipway onto beach available for 3 hours either side HW. No fuel or toilets, parking for car and trailer (c). Speed limit 6 knots inshore. No Charge.

Ryde
Appley Slip
Site is at east end of Northwalk at Appley Park. Concrete slipway onto beach available for 3 hours either side HW. No fuel, parking for car and trailer (c), toilets. Speed limit 6 knots inshore. No Charge.

Seaview
Springvale Slip
Follow B 3340 from Ryde: site is opposite Battery Hotel and access is via Springvale Rd. Concrete slipway available for 3 hours either side HW. No fuel or parking, toilets, nearest chandlers in Bembridge. Speed limit 6 knots inshore. No Charge.

Seaview
Esplanade
Follow B 3340 from Ryde and signs to seafront: site is at junction of High St and Esplanade on sharp bend. Steep concrete slipway with sharp bend onto shingle is available for 3 hours either side HW and suitable small craft only. No fuel, no parking or toilets. Speed limit 6 knots inshore. No Charge.

Seaview
Pier Road
Follow B 3340 from Ryde turning off High St into Pier Rd. Concrete slipway at end of road available for 3 hours either side HW. No fuel, parking for car and trailer, no toilets. Speed limit 6 knots inshore. No Charge.

Seagrove Bay
Follow B 3330 from Ryde: site is at southern end of bay and access is via Gully Rd. Concrete slipway available for 3 hours either side HW. No fuel or parking, toilets, nearest chandlers in Bembridge. Speed limit 6 knots inshore. No Charge.

The Duver, St Helens
H Attrill & Sons (IoW) Ltd
From Ryde take B 3330 to St Helens and private road across the Duver. Concrete slipway available 3 hours either side HW. Diesel, parking for car and trailer (c). Speed limit 6 knots inshore. Charge.

St Helens Duver
Follow B 3330 from Ryde and signs to The Duver: access is through car park (c). Concrete slipway is available for 3 hours either side HW. No fuel, parking for car and trailer (c), toilets, café. Speed limit 6 knots inshore. No Charge.

Bembridge Harbour
Bembridge Outboards, Embankment Rd
Take A 3055 and B 3330 from Ryde: access is via Embankment Rd on south shore of harbour. Concrete slipway available 2½ hours either side HW suitable dinghies and powerboats. Petrol (¼ mile), parking for car and trailer, toilets, chandlery from Spinnaker Yacht Chandlery. Yard specialises in outboards and welcomes visitors with powerboats. Speed limit 6 knots inshore. Check for availability Tel Bembridge(0983) 872817. Charge.

HAMPSHIRE

Calshot Spit
Calshot Activities Centre
From Southampton, follow A 326 and B 3053: site is signposted. The centre is an ex-RAF flying boat base. Two slipways, one concrete, the other tarmac on concrete available during daylight hours at all states of tide except perhaps for ½ hour either side LWS suitable all craft. Fuel from garage (1 mile) or from Hamble Point Marina, ample parking for car and trailer (c), toilets and showers, chandlery from Southampton or Hamble, boat storage facilities. Site gives excellent access to sheltered waters of the Solent. Keep well clear of busy shipping channels: all boats must have 3rd party insurance. No speed limit: water-skiing allowed in designated areas in Solent. Further information Tel Fawley(0703) 892077. Charge.

Southampton Water
This is a busy stretch of water: do not obstruct large vessels which have to keep to the buoyed deep-water channel. There is a speed limit north of Hythe Pier and in the Itchen river of 6 knots. Water-skiing is allowed in designated areas but not in the Itchen.

Fawley (Southampton Water)
Ashlett Creek
Follow A 326 turning off to Ashlett. Shingle hard available for 3 hours either side HW. No fuel, parking for car and trailer, toilets, pub. Charge.

Hythe (Southampton Water)
Hythe Marina Village
Follow A 326 Southampton to Fawley road and signs to marina and slipway. Concrete slipway available for approx 4 hours either side HW and suitable all craft: site gives access directly into Southampton Water. Fuel, parking for car and trailer, toilets, telephone, chandlery from Shamrock Chandlery: all facilities available from marina adjacent. No Charge.

Marchwood (Southampton Water)
Cracknore Hard
From Southampton, follow A 326, turning left to Marchwood and go through Husbands Shipyard. Shingle hard available for 4 hours either side HW. No fuel, parking, leave trailer by arrangement with yard. No Charge.

Eling Creek (Southampton Water)
Eling Wharf
From Southampton follow signs to Eling Village: site is adjacent to the Anchor Inn. Steep shingle hard with "drop-off" at the bottom available for 3 hours either side HW. Fuel, parking for car and trailer (c), no toilets. No Charge.

River Itchen
Crosshouse Hard, Chapel
Site is on west side of the river, just north of the Itchen Bridge: access is via Crosshouse Rd. Concrete slipway and gravel hard available at most states of tide. No fuel, parking for car and trailer (not overnight), no toilets. This site is likely to be improved in the future. No Charge.

River Itchen
Priory Hard, St Denys
From city centre follow signs to St Denys Station: site is on west side of river south of the station: access is via Priory Rd. Concrete slipway and gravel hard available at most states of tide. No fuel, parking for car and trailer, no toilets. No Charge.

River Itchen
Itchen Ferry Hard, Woolston
Leave M 27 at junction 8 and follow A 3025: from city centre cross Itchen Bridge; site is on east side of river just north of the bridge and access is via Hazel Rd. Concrete slipway and gravel hard available at most states of tide. No fuel, parking for car and trailer (not overnight), no toilets, chandlery from Gerard Goulding. No Charge.

River Itchen
Victoria Road Slipway, Woolston
Leave M 27 at junction 8 taking A 3025 to Woolston: site is south of bridge and access is via Victoria Rd. Concrete slipway and gravel hard available at most states of tide. No fuel, parking for car and trailer, no toilets, chandlery from Gerrard Goulding. Apply for permission to use from Director of Leisure Services, Civic Centre, Southampton Tel Southampton (0703) 223855 ext 2314. No Charge.

Weston (Southampton Water)
Weston Shore Slipway
Leave M 27 at junction 8 and follow A 3025: site is on Weston Shore and access is via Weston Parade. No fuel, parking for car and trailer (not overnight), toilets. No Charge.

Netley Abbey (Southampton Water)
Beach Lane Slipway
Leave M 27 at junction 8 and follow A 3025 turning off to Netley Abbey: site is approached via Victoria Rd. Concrete slipway onto shingle available for 2 hours either side HW and suitable small craft only. Fuel in village, parking for car and trailer, toilets. No Charge.

Netley Abbey (Southampton Water)
Victoria Road Slipway
Leave M 27 at junction 8 and follow A 3025, turning off to follow signs to Royal Victoria Country Park: site is outside entrance. Concrete slipway onto soft shingle available for 2 hours either side HW and suitable small craft only. Fuel in village, parking for car and trailer. No Charge.

Hamble River
Sheltered but crowded waters giving access to the Solent via Southampton Water. Speed limit 5 knots: no water-skiing in river.

Hamble Quay, High Street (River Hamble)
Leave M 27 at junction 8 and follow B 3397 to Hamble: site is at end of High St next to Royal Southern YC and opposite the Bugle Inn. Concrete hard for dinghies accessible only through locked dinghy pound: Foreshore Warden with key is in attendance at weekends, or shingle hard available for approx 4 hours either side HW. Fuel in village or at marinas, limited parking for car and trailer (often congested), toilets, chandlery from Compass Point Chandlers. This is a popular and busy site. No Charge.

Port Hamble Marina (River Hamble)
Leave M 27 at junction 8 following B 3397 and signs to marina. Concrete slipway available at all states of tide. Fuel, limited parking for car and trailer (c), toilets, chandlery. Check for availablity Tel Southampton(0703) 452741. Charge

Mercury Yacht Harbour (River Hamble)
Leave M 27 at junction 8 following B 3397 and signs to marina. Concrete slipway available up to 1 hour either side LWS. Fuel, parking for car and trailer (c), toilets, chandlery and all other facilities. Check for availability Tel Southampton(0703) 452741. Charge.

Lands End Road, Bursledon (River Hamble)
Leave M 27 at junction 8 following A 27 to Bursledon turning right in village towards Bursledon Pt: site is opposite Moody's Boatyard and close to "The Jolly Sailor". Shingle foreshore available at all states of tide suitable for launching dinghies only. Fuel from marinas, parking (½ mile) at station, chandlery from Aladdin's Cave. No Charge.

Lower Swanick (River Hamble)
Leave M 27 at junction 9, following the A 27: site is just downstream of Moody's Boatyard. Shingle hard available at all states of tide. Fuel and chandlery from marina, limited parking. No Charge.

Warsash (River Hamble)
Leave M 27 at junction 9 and follow A 27, then minor roads: site is opposite "The Rising Sun". Shingle hard available at all states of tide. Diesel only from Warsash Boat Centre, parking for car (c) with limited space for trailers, toilets, chandlery from Sea Fever Yacht Chandlery. No Charge.

Lee-on-Solent
Marine Parade East
Leave M 27 at junction 11, taking A 27 and B 3385 to seafront. Steep concrete slipway available for 4 hours either side HW. No fuel, parking for car and trailer (c), toilets, chandlers in Gosport. Speed limit 7 knots within 1000yds of beach: water-skiing in designated area. No Charge.

Lee-on-Solent
Solent Gardens
Leave M 27 at junction 11 taking A 27 and B 3385 to seafront. Concrete slipway onto shingle available for 2½ hours either side HW or launch over shingle at all times. No fuel, parking for car and trailer (c), toilets, nearest chandlers in Gosport. Speed limit 7 knots within 1000yds beach: water-skiing in designated area. No Charge.

Stokes Bay
Leave M 27 at junction 11, taking A 27 and B 3385/B 3333 to seafront. Three well-marked sites, the best being at No 2 battery. All sites have concrete slipways which are available for direct launching for 4 hours either side HW or for launching over shingle at all times. No fuel, parking for car and trailer (c), toilets. Speed limit 10 knots within ½ mile of shore: designated water-skiing area off Lee-on-Solent. No Charge.

Portsmouth Harbour

Portsmouth is a busy naval and ferry port and the entrance can become very busy. There is a 10 knot speed limit in the harbour and water-skiing is not allowed. The harbour is under the jurisdiction of the Queen's Harbour Master Tel Portsmouth(0705) 22351 ext 2008.

Hardway, Gosport, (Portsmouth Harbour)

Leave M 27 at junction 11, taking A 32 Gosport road and following signs: site is adjacent 105 Priory Road. Steep concrete slipway available for 4½ hours either side HW and suitable all types of craft. Diesel, parking for car and trailer, toilets in car park, chandlery from Hardway Marine, pub. No Charge.

Lower Quay, Fareham (Portsmouth Harbour)

Leave M 27 at junction 11, taking A 27: site is adjacent Lower Quay. Concrete slipway available for 2 hours either side HW. Fuel from local garage, parking for car and trailer, no toilets, chandlery from Fareham Marine adjacent. No Charge.

Paulsgrove (Portsmouth Harbour)

Leave M 27 at junction 11, taking A 27 eastbound and turning off at signpost to "Royal Navy Firefighting School". Concrete slipway available 2½ hours either side HW. No fuel, parking limited, no toilets, nearest chandlers at Fareham. No Charge.

Portsmouth
Camber Quay, East Street

Follow signs to Old Portsmouth from M 27/M 275: site is old Isle of Wight ferry slip. Wide concrete slipway into deep water available at all states of tide. No fuel, parking for car and trailer, toilets, chandlers nearby. Speed limit 7 knots. Lockable barrier on main slip is closed from 1700-0800 Mon to Fri: for opening times at weekends contact the Berthing Master Tel Portsmouth(0705) 834764. Take care when leaving slip. Charge.

Langstone Harbour

A large area of sheltered but fairly shallow water. There is a speed limit of 10 knots: water-skiing is allowed in a designated area in Langstone Channel under licence (1st Apr-30th Sept). The Harbour Master's Office is at Ferry Pt on Hayling Is Tel Hayling Is(0705) 463419. It is forbidden to land on any of the islands in the harbour. Harbour dues are payable.

Eastney Beach (Langstone Harbour)

From M 27/A 27 follow A 2030 and signs to Southsea, turning off to follow signs to Hayling Is ferry: site is just south of Eastney CA Clubhouse. Concrete slipway available at all states of tide. Fuel from Harbour Office at Ferry Pt, parking for car and trailer, toilets, nearest chandlers Chris Hornsey in Eastney. No Charge but harbour dues payable.

Brockhampton Quay, Havant (Langstone Harbour)

Leave A 27 at Bedhampton, crossing south over A 27 and following signs to Industrial Estate: site is just before Brockhampton Quay and after reclaimed tipping site: access is via unmade road. Wide concrete slipway available at all states of tide. No fuel, parking for car and trailer, no toilets, nearest chandlers in Havant. No Charge but harbour dues payable.

Ferry Point, Hayling Island (Langstone Harbour)

From A 27 follow signs to Hayling Island: site is on western tip of island and adjacent to Harbour Office and Ferry Boat Inn. Wide concrete slipway available at all states of tide. Fuel from Harbour Board premises, parking for car (c), trailer can be left at harbour board premises, toilets, pub, chandlers nearby. Site becomes congested in summer season. Recovery on slipway can be difficult at LW: seek advice from Harbour Office. A recovery vehicle is available. No Charge but harbour dues payable.

Chichester Harbour

One of the most attractive and popular of the south coast harbours with 11 square miles of water. Tides run strongly in the harbour and especially in the narrow entrance where speeds of up to 5.3 knots on the ebb at springs may be experienced. There is a speed limit of 8 knots in the harbour and water-skiing is not allowed. Landing on Thorney and Pilsey Is (MOD property) is forbidden above the MHW line. All boats have to pay harbour dues: the harbour is a conservation area and should be treated with respect. Further information from the Harbour Office at Itchenor Tel Birdham(0243) 512301.

Sandy Point, Hayling Island (Chichester Harbour)
Sparkes Boatyard, 38 Wittering Road

Leave A 27 and follow signs to Hayling Is: site is at eastern tip of island close to Hayling Island SC. Concrete slipway available for 3 hours either side HW and suitable craft up to 25'LOA. Fuel, parking for car and trailer (c), toilets, chandlery and full boatyard facilities on site. Check for availability Tel Hayling Is(0705) 463572/465741. Charge and harbour dues payable.

Hayling Island (Chichester Harbour)
Hayling Yacht Co Ltd, Mill Rythe

Leave A 27 and follow signs to Hayling Is: site is on east of island after 2 miles. Concrete slipway available for 2 hours either side HW suitable all types of craft. Fuel, parking for car and trailer, crane and hoist available for hire, toilets and chandlery on site, also repair and storage facilities. Check for availability Tel Hayling Is(0705) 463592. Charge and harbour dues payable.

Northney (Chichester Harbour)
Northney Marina

Leave A 27 and follow signs to Hayling Is, turning left immediately after crossing bridge. Two concrete slipways: one into the marina is available at all times and is suitable all types of craft; the other into the harbour is available for 4 hours either side HW and is suitable small craft. Fuel, parking for car and trailer, toilets, chandlery and other facilities on site. For further information Tel Hayling(0705) 467334. This site gives acess to sheltered waters ideal for day sailers and windsurfers. Charge and harbour dues payable.

Langstone (Chichester Harbour)
Ship Inn

Leave A 27 and follow signs to Hayling Is: site is on the left just before the bridge and adjacent Ship Inn. Concrete slipway available for 3 hours either side HW and suitable small craft only. Fuel from garage over bridge, parking for car and trailer, toilets in pub, nearest chandlers in Havant. This site gives access to sheltered waters ideal for day sailers and windsurfers. No Charge but harbour dues payable.

Warblington Road (Chichester Harbour)

Turn off A 27 just west of Emsworth into Warblington Rd. Shingle hard at end of road is available for 3 hours either side HW and suitable small craft only. No fuel, limited parking and turning in road, nearest toilets, and chandlers in Emsworth. No Charge but harbour dues payable.

Emsworth (Chichester Harbour)
South Street

Turn off A 27 into Emsworth. Concrete slipway onto shingle is available for 2 hours either side HW. No fuel, parking and toilets in car park at top of street, chandlery from Sea Teach chandlers opposite. Site can be very congested in summer. No Charge but harbour dues payable.

SUSSEX

Emsworth Yacht Harbour (Chichester Harbour)

Follow sign off A 27 east of Emsworth: site is at top of Thorney Is. Concrete slipway available for 2½ hours either side HW. Fuel, parking for car and trailer (c), toilets. Charge and harbour dues payable.

Prinsted (Chichester Harbour)

Follow sign off A 27 east of Emsworth: site is at end of road south of village. Shingle hard available for 2/3 hours launching into the Thorney Channel and suitable small craft only. No fuel or toilets, limited parking for car and trailer. No Charge but harbour dues payable.

Bosham (Chichester Harbour)
Bosham Lane

Follow signs from A 27: site is at end of Bosham Lane. Shingle foreshore available for 3 hours either side HW suitable small craft only. Fuel from garage on main road, parking for car and trailer (c) and toilets in car park in Bosham Lane. No Charge but harbour dues payable.

Bosham (Chichester Harbour)
The Quay

Follow signs from A 27 and foreshore road to quay: access is often congested. Concrete slipway onto shingle and mud available for 3 hours either side HW. Fuel from garage on main road, no parking on quay but car park (c) and toilets in Bosham Lane. Charge (pay Quaymaster) and harbour dues payable.

Dell Quay (Chichester Harbour)

Turn off A 27 onto A 286 following signs to Dell Quay: site is at end of road and adjacent Quay. Shingle hard available for 2½ hours either side HW. No fuel, limited parking, pub. No Charge but harbour dues payable.

Birdham (Chichester Harbour)
Chichester Yacht Basin

Turn off A 27 onto A 286 and turn off to Yacht Basin when signposted: concrete slipway into locked basin available at all times and suitable all sizes craft. Fuel from jetty nearby, parking, trailers can be stored at boatyard (c), toilets, chandlery from Yacht and Sports Gear, shops and boatyard facilities. Check availability Tel Chichester(0243) 512731. Charge and harbour dues payable.

Itchenor (Chichester Harbour)

Turn off A 27 onto A 286 turning off to Itchenor after approx 8 miles: site is at end of road. Shingle hard available at all states of tide and suitable all craft. No fuel, chandlery from H C Darley, parking for car and trailer (c) in car park, toilets below Harbour Office. Charge and harbour dues payable.

Bracklesham

Turn off A 27 onto A 286, turning off onto B 2198: site is at end of road. Concrete slipway onto hard beach available at all states of tide. No fuel, parking for car and trailer, toilets, nearest chandlers H C Darley at Itchenor. Tractor assisted launching is available (c) for larger craft: vehicles other than licensed tractors not permitted on beach. No Charge.

Selsey
East Beach

Turn off A 27 onto B 2145: site is signposted from main street. Wooden ramp to shingle beach available for 2/3 hours either side HW. Fuel from local garage, parking for car and trailer (c), toilets, no chandlers. There are strong currents in this area and this site is not suitable in onshore winds. No Charge.

Bognor Regis
Gloucester Road

Follow A 27 east from Chichester, turning onto A 259 and B 2166 and follow signs to seafront: site is at east end and access is via car park. Concrete ramp with wooden sides available at all states of tide. Fuel from garage (¼ mile, not Sun), parking for car and trailer (c), toilets, nearest chandlers (½ mile). Speed limit 8 knots in buoyed area within 300m of MLW mark: water-skiing is permitted outside this area. Further information from Foreshore Station opposite pier Tel Bognor Regis(0243) 861821. No Charge.

River Arun

Tides run strongly in the river and especially in the entrance where rates of up to 6 knots can be experienced at springs. There is a speed limit of 6½ knots in the river and board-sailing and water-skiing are not allowed. Harbour dues are payable at the Harbour Office Tel Littlehampton(0903) 721215.

Littlehampton (River Arun)
Littlehampton Marina, Ferry Road

From Arundel follow A 284 and A 259, crossing the river and turning left ½ mile further on: site is on west bank, downstream of bridge and 1 mile from the sea. Launching by yard staff only available from 4 hours before to 5 hours after HW and suitable all craft. Fuel, parking for car and trailer, crane, toilets and showers, chandlery, diving and yard facilities. Check for availability Tel Littlehampton(0903) 713553. Charge.

Littlehampton (River Arun)
Fishermans Quay, Surrey Street

Follow A 284 from Arundel and signs to town centre: site is at end of Surrey St on east bank. Steep concrete slipway (1:6) onto mud available at all states of tide but best near HW due to gradient of slipway. Fuel from local garage or marina, parking for car and trailer under 14' only (c), toilets in town centre, chandlery and tractor (for hire) from Britannia Watersports adjacent. No Charge

Worthing
Sea Place Car Park, Marine Crescent

From A 27 or A 24 follow signs to sea front: site is in Marine Crescent. Wooden ramp onto shingle beach available for 3 hours either side HW: access from car park has height restriction of 4'6''. Fuel from local garages, parking for car and trailer, toilets, chandlery from Sea Place Marine. Speed limit 8 knots during summer: water-skiing allowed outside 275m from LW mark. It may be difficult to launch in strong onshore winds and car park becomes very congested in summer. Vehicles are not allowed on the promenade so boats must be manhandled. No Charge.

Worthing
Alinora Car Park, Marine Crescent

From A 27 or A 24 follow signs to sea front: site is in Marine Crescent. Wooden ramp onto shingle beach available for 3 hours either side HW: access from car park has height restriction of 5'. Fuel from local garages, parking for car and trailer, toilets in Sea Place, chandlery from Sea Place Marine. Speed limit 8 knots during summer: water-skiing allowed outside 275m from LW mark. It can be difficult to launch in onshore winds and car park becomes very crowded in summer. Vehicles are not allowed on the promenade so craft must be manhandled. No Charge.

Shoreham (River Adur)
Ropetackle, Little High St Hard

From A 24 follow A 283 to Shoreham, turning right after Ballamys' Garage into Little High St. Site is upstream of the Norfolk Bridge. Concrete road onto shingle and mud available for 2/3 hours either side HW suitable dinghies and powerboats. Fuel, parking for car and trailer (c), chandlers and boatyard nearby. Speed limit 4 knots, speedboats 10 knots: no water-skiing in harbour. No Charge but harbour dues payable.

Shoreham Harbour
Shoreham Car Auctions, Kingston Wharf

Turn off A 259 Worthing to Brighton road. Concrete slipway available at all states of tide suitable all types of craft. Fuel, parking for car and trailer (c), winch: towing vehicles and assisted launching are available on request. Speed limit 4 knots in harbour: water-skiing allowed offshore. For further information Tel Shoreham(0273) 594309/595250. Charge and harbour dues payable.

Shoreham Harbour
Lady Bee Marina, Albion Street
Turn off A 27 onto A 283 and A 259: site is in Southwick opposite Pilot Pub. Concrete and steel slipway into locked harbour available during normal business hours but subject to lock gates opening 4 hours either side HW. Diesel from chandlers, petrol from local garage, limited parking, toilets, chandlery from G P Barnes. Check for availability Tel Shoreham(0273) 593801/591705.Charge.

Newhaven (River Ouse)
Newhaven Marina
Turn off A 27 onto A 26 and follow one-way system, turning left at Police Station: site is on west bank of River Ouse, 350yds from harbour entrance. Concrete slipway available for 4 hours either side HW from 0800- 1700 and suitable shallow-draught craft with engines only, up to 20'LOA and 1½ tons max. Fuel, parking for car and trailer, toilets, chandlery from Russell Simpson Marine, visitors' berths. Speed limit in harbour entrance: water-skiing allowed offshore. Tractor assisted launching only: check for availability Tel Newhaven(0273) 513881. Charge.

Eastbourne
Prince William Parade
Site is at exteme eastern end of the seafront road: access is through height restriction barrier (7' 3'' high 12' wide). Launching over shingle beach available at all times and suitable small craft which can be manhandled. Fuel, parking for car and trailer, winch, no toilets. No Charge.

Note: launching from all other beaches in the Eastbourne area is prohibited except to members of recognised clubs.

Bexhill-on-Sea
West Parade
Turn off A 21 onto A 259 and follow signs to seafront. Concrete slipway onto shingle beach available at all states of tide but best for 4 hours either side HW. Fuel from local garage, parking for car and trailer, toilets nearby. Speed limit 8 knots within 100m of the shore. No Charge.

Rye Harbour (River Rother)
Rye Harbour Village
Follow A 259 from Hastings or Folkestone, turning off to Rye Harbour. Concrete slipway available from 2 hours before to 3 hours after HW and suitable all craft up to 40'LOA. Petrol from local garage, diesel and chandlery from Sandrock Marine (3 miles), parking for car and trailer, toilets, telephone. Speed limit 6 knots in river and dead slow through moorings: water-skiing in river only allowed for members of Rye Water-Ski Club or one mile offshore for non-members. Further information from Harbour Master Tel Rye(0797) 225225. Charge and harbour dues payable. **Note:** narrow harbour entrance with bar and strong tidal flow: vessels must not enter or leave the harbour against the direction of the Harbour Master.

KENT

Folkestone
Inner Harbour Slipway
Follow M 20 to Folkestone: access is through low bridge arches by the fish stalls. Concrete slipway available for 3 hours either side HW. Fuel, parking for car and trailer nearby, toilets, chandlery from Bosuns Locker. Speed limit in harbour: water-skiing allowed offshore. No Charge.

Dover Harbour
Marine Parade
Follow A 2 to Eastern Docks, then along Marine Parade: site is opposite Royal Cinque Ports YC. Concrete slipway available at all states of tide and suitable dinghies and larger craft if trailers can be manhandled: road vehicles are not allowed on the Promenade which runs between the road and the slipway. Fuel, parking for car (c), toilets and showers, telephone, chandlery from Dover Marine Supplies, Snargate St: yard facilities from Dover Yacht Co. Speed limit 8 knots: no water-skiing. Any boat wishing to leave the harbour must call Dover Port Control on VHF Ch 74/12 for permission or contact the Harbour Patrol Launch. No Charge.

St Margaret's Bay
St Margaret's at Cliffe
Follow A 258 Deal Road from A 2, at top of Jubilee Way and signs. Wooden ramp onto beach available at all states of tide but best at HW and suitable small craft. No fuel, parking for car and trailer (c), toilets, refreshments, nearest chandlers in Dover. Speed limit 10mph within 150m of LW mark. No Charge.

Deal
Kingsdown
Follow A 258 and B 2057 from M 2/A 2. Wooden ramp onto shingle available at all states of tide but best near HW. No fuel, parking for car and trailer, no toilets, nearest chandlers in Dover. Speed limit: water-skiing allowed beyond 150m from LW mark with access by buoyed channels. No Charge.

Deal
North End Ramps
Follow A 258 from A 2/M 2. Two concrete slipways available at all states of tide. No fuel, restricted parking for cars only. Speed limit: water-skiing allowed beyond 150m from LW mark with access channels. Access to site closed in winter due to possible flooding. No Charge.

Sandwich (River Stour)
Town Quay
Follow A 257 east from Canterbury following signs to town centre. Concrete slipway available for two hours either side HW and suitable small craft. Fuel from local garage, parking for car and trailer (c), toilets, chandlery and boatyard facilities from Highway Marine. Speed limit 6mph in river: water-skiing permitted in open sea. No Charge.

Ramsgate Harbour
Harbour
Follow M 2/A 299/A 253 and signs to ferry terminal. Granite block slipway into locked inner harbour available at all states of tide and suitable all craft: lock gates open from 2 hours before to 2 hours after HW. Fuel, parking for car and trailer (c), tractor, toilets and chandlers in Military Rd. Speed limit 5 knots in harbour: no water-skiing in harbour: 12 ton crane is available. Get Harbour Master's permission to launch Tel Ramsgate(0843) 592277. Charge.

Ramsgate
Eastern Undercliff (Winterstoke Undercliff)
Follow M 2/A 299, A 253 and local signs. Concrete slipway available at all states of tide. Fuel from garage ($\frac{1}{2}$ mile), parking for car and trailer, toilets. This is a designated area for water-skiing. Access to site may be obstructed. No Charge. **Note:** For further information on launching facilities in the Ramsgate area contact J McCarthy, Water Safety Officer Tel Thanet(0843) 225511 ext 2560.

Broadstairs Harbour
Follow A 255 from Margate or Ramsgate. Two slipways, one concrete and one wood are available for $2\frac{1}{2}$ hours either side HW. Fuel from garage ($\frac{1}{2}$ mile), parking for car and trailer, toilets, nearest chandlers in Ramsgate. Speed limit 5 knots within harbour and 8 knots within 400m HW mark. Charge.

46

47

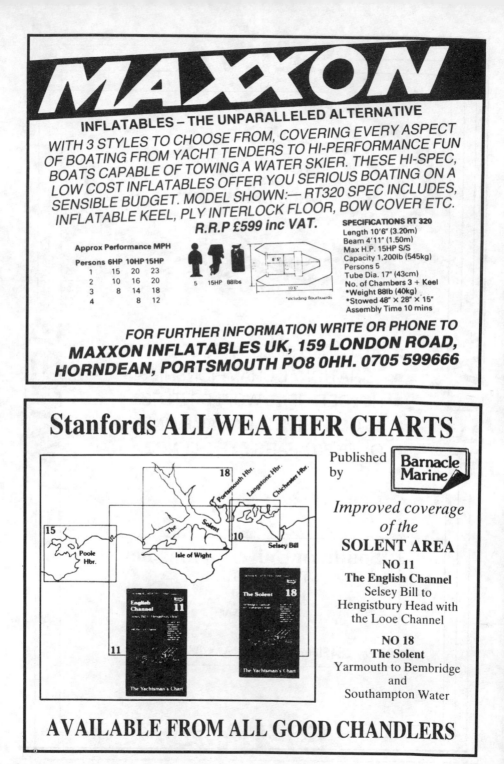

49

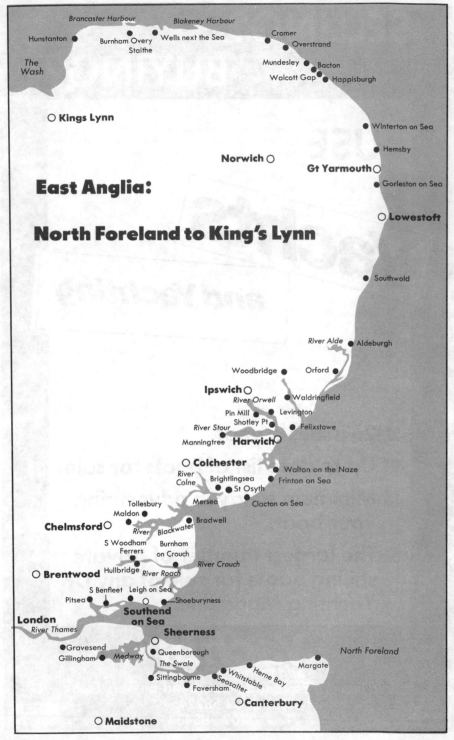

East Anglia:

North Foreland to King's Lynn

The Wash

Hunstanton
Brancaster Harbour
Burnham Overy Staithe
Wells next the Sea
Blakeney Harbour
Cromer
Overstrand
Mundesley
Bacton
Walcott Gap
Happisburgh

O Kings Lynn

Winterton on Sea

Hemsby

Norwich O

Gt Yarmouth O

Gorleston on Sea

O Lowestoft

Southwold

River Alde
Aldeburgh

Woodbridge
Orford

Ipswich O
River Orwell
Waldringfield
Pin Mill
Levington
Shotley Pt
River Stour
Felixstowe
Manningtree
Harwich O

O Colchester

River Colne
Brightlingsea
Walton on the Naze
Frinton on Sea
St Osyth
Mersea
Clacton on Sea

Tollesbury
Maldon
Bradwell
Chelmsford O
River Blackwater
S Woodham Ferrers
Burnham on Crouch
Hullbridge
River Crouch
O Brentwood
River Roach
S Benfleet
Leigh on Sea
Pitsea
Shoeburyness
London
Southend on Sea
River Thames
Sheerness
Gravesend
Queenborough
North Foreland
Gillingham
Medway
The Swale
Margate
Sittingbourne
Whitstable
Herne Bay
Faversham
Seasalter

O Canterbury

O Maidstone

KENT

Visitors to the Isle of Thanet who wish to water-ski should contact the Foreshore and Recreation Officer Tel Thanet(0843) 225511 who will put them in touch with the local ski club. Water-skiing must be done only from slipways in designated areas and skiers must obey local bye-laws.

Margate
Palm Bay (Foreness Bay)
Follow A 28 from Canterbury to seafront at Cliftonville, east of Margate town. Concrete slipway onto beach available at all states of tide but best for 2 hours either side HW. Fuel from garage (1 mile), parking for car and trailer, toilets, chandlers in Margate. This area is operated by the Foreness Ski Club and is a designated water-skiing area: other activities are not permitted. No Charge.

Margate Harbour
Harbour Slip
Follow A 28 from Canterbury. Concrete slipway onto sand available for 2 hours either side HW. Fuel from garage ($\frac{1}{4}$ mile), parking for car and trailer (c) and toilets adjacent to yacht club, chandlers in town. Speed limit 8 knots within 400m HW mark: water-skiing allowed in designated areas. Margate YC offers temporary membership to visitors. Charge.

Margate
Westbrook Bay
Follow A 28 from Canterbury to Westbrook, west of Margate town. Concrete slipway onto firm sand available at all states of tide but best for 2 hours either side HW. Fuel from garage ($\frac{1}{2}$ mile), parking for car and trailer (c), toilets, chandlers in Margate. This area is operated by the Westbrook Ski Club and is a designated water-skiing area: other activities are not permitted. No Charge.

Margate
St Mildreds Bay
Follow A 28 from Canterbury to seafront at Westgate-on-Sea. Concrete slipway onto firm sand available at all states of tide but best for 2 hours either side HW. Fuel from garage ($\frac{1}{2}$ mile), parking for car (c) but not trailer, toilets, chandlers in Margate. This site is for small sailing boats and boats with engines under 15 HP only: water-skiing is not allowed. The tide goes out a long way here and vehicles are not allowed on the beach. No Charge.

Margate
West Bay, Westgate, East Ramp
Follow A 28 from Canterbury to seafront at Westgate-on-Sea. Concrete slipway onto firm sand available at all states of tide but best for 2 hours either side HW. Fuel nearby, no parking on promenade, toilets, chandlers in Margate. Site is for dinghies only: power boats and water-skiing are not allowed. No Charge.

Margate
Beresford Gap, Birchington
Follow A 28 from Canterbury and signs to seafront. Concrete slipway onto firm sand available at all states of tide but best 2 hours either side HW. Fuel from garage (1 mile), parking for car and trailer on promenade, toilets, chandlers in Margate. This area is operated by the Beresford Ski Club and is a designated water-skiing area: other activities are not permitted. No Charge.

Margate
Minnis Bay, Birchington
Follow A 28 from Canterbury and signs to seafront. Concrete slipway onto firm sand available at all states of tide but best 2 hours either side HW. Fuel from garage (1 mile), parking for car (c) but not trailer, toilets, chandlers in Margate. Site is for sailing dinghies and small craft only. Speed limit 8 knots within 400m HW mark: no water-skiing. No Charge.

Herne Bay
Neptune Jetty, Central Parade
From Canterbury, follow A 28 and B 291 and signs to seafront. Site is east of Pier, near the Clock Tower and opposite the Bun Penny Pub. Concrete slipway available for 3/4 hours either side HW and suitable fishing boats and dinghies. Fuel from local garages, limited car parking on Central Parade or in William St car park (c), trailers can be left at edge of slipway, toilets, chandlery from Herne Bay Seasports. Speed limit 8 knots inshore: no water-skiing. Site is exposed in northerly winds. No Charge.

Herne Bay
Hampton, Swalecliffe Avenue
Follow B 2205 west from Herne Bay, turning from Hampton Pier Ave into Swalecliffe Ave. Concrete slipway with stepped slope onto mud and shingle available for 2 hours either side HW and suitable power craft. Fuel from local garage, parking for car and trailer, toilets and café on site. Herne Bay Water Ski Club is adjacent and this is a designated water-ski area with buoyed access lane from slipway. Speed limit 8 knots inshore. Take care to avoid rocky patch marked by beacons. No Charge.

Whitstable
From A 299 follow A 290 and B 2205: site is on west side of harbour. Concrete slipway available for 3 hours either side HW and suitable all craft and trailers up to 1 ton axle weight. Fuel from local garage, parking for car and trailer nearby, toilets, chandlery from Roy Rigden & Partners. Speed limit 8 knots within 400m of the HW mark: water-skiing permitted outside this limit. Further information from the Harbour Master Tel Whitstable(0227) 274086. No Charge (under review).

Whitstable
Roy Rigden & Partners
Follow M 2 and A 299/A 290: site is on sea wall, just west of the harbour. Concrete slipway onto shingle available for 2/3 hours either side HW. Fuel from garage, parking for car and trailer (c), toilets, chandlery. Speed limit 8 knots within 400m HW mark: water-skiing permitted outside this limit. Check for availability Tel Whitstable(0227) 266268. Charge.

Whitstable Harbour
Timothy Carpenter Boatyard, Sea Wall
Follow M 2 and A 299/A 290. Concrete slipway onto shingle available at all states of tide and suitable for craft up to 21'LOA. Fuel from garage, parking for car and trailer (c), toilets, chandlery. Speed limit 8 knots inshore: water-skiing in designated areas. Check for availability Tel Whitstable(0227) 262525. Charge.

Seasalter
Alberta Car Park
Turn off A 299 west of Whitstable and follow signs to Seasalter. Access to site is through public car park adjacent Seasalter Water Ski Club. Launch over steep shingle bank onto sandy beach at HW. No fuel, parking for car and trailer (c). Speed limit 8 knots inshore: water-skiing in designated areas only. No Charge.

Faversham (The Swale)
Wharf Boatyard, Belvedere Road
Leave M 2 at junction 6 following signs to town centre. Concrete slipway into Faversham Ck available for 2 hours either side HW suitable for launching dinghies. Fuel, parking for car and trailer (c), toilets and showers, chandlery from Faversham Chandlery, boatyard facilities on site. Speed limit in Faversham Ck: no water-skiing. Charge.

Harty Ferry (The Swale)
Old Ferry Slipway
Leave M 2 at junction 6 following signs to Oare, then Harty Ferry two miles north of Faversham. Concrete slipway onto shingle available for 2/3 hours either side HW. No fuel, limited parking for car and trailer, no toilets. Speed limit 8 knots inshore. No Charge.

Jarman's Boatyard (The Swale)
Conyer Wharf, Teynham
Turn off A 2 between Sittingbourne and Faversham and follow signs. Concrete slipway into Conyer Ck available for 2½/3 hours either side HW and suitable all craft. Fuel, ample parking for car and trailer (c), toilets, chandlery and boatyard facilities on site. Speed limit 8 knots. Check for availability Tel Teynham(0795) 521562. Charge.

Sittingbourne (The Swale)
Kingsferry Bridge
Leave M 2 at junction 5 following A 249 to Isle of Sheppey: site is on mainland side of bridge: follow signs to Ridham Dock. Concrete slipway available for 2 hours either side HW. No fuel, parking for car and trailer (c), no toilets. Speed limit 8 knots: water-skiing allowed in Long Reach. Charge.

Queenborough (The Swale)
Queenborough Hard, Isle of Sheppey
Leave M 2 at junction 5 following the A 249 to the Isle of Sheppey: access is via the High St. Concrete slipway onto shingle available for 2 hours either side HW and suitable all craft up to 20'LOA. Fuel from local garages, parking for car and trailer (c), toilets, chandlery from Bosun's Store, High St. Speed limit 8 knots: no water-skiing. Charge.

Shingle Bank (The Medway)
Barton Point, Marine Parade, Sheerness
Follow A 249 to Sheerness: access to site is via Marine Parade. Launching over shingle available at all states of tide but best near HW and suitable small craft only. No fuel, parking for car and trailer, toilets at White House, Scrapsgate Rd. Speed limit 8 knots inshore. No Charge.

Minster, Isle of Sheppey (Thames Estuary)
Leave M 2 at junction 5 following the A 249 to Sheerness Clock Tower, then right along Marine Parade for 1¼ miles. Concrete slipway onto shingle available for 2 hours either side HW and suitable for dinghies. Fuel from local garages, parking for car and trailer (c), toilets. Speed limit 8 knots: water-skiing in designated areas. Charge.

Gillingham (River Medway)
Gillingham Pier
Leave M 2 at junction 4 taking A 278/A 2 and B 2004: access is via Pier Approach Rd. Concrete slipway available for 2 hours either side HW. Fuel, parking for car and trailer. Speed limit 6 knots inshore. Charge.

Gillingham (River Medway)
Commodore Hard, Pier
Access is via the B 2004. Concrete slipway available at all states of tide and suitable craft up to 24'LOA. Fuel, parking for car only, toilets, chandlery and yard facilities from Gillingham Marina. Speed limit 6 knots. No Charge.

Gillingham (River Medway)
Gillingham Marina
Leave M 2 at junction 4 taking A 2 and B 2004: access is via Pier Rd. Launching by boat hoist only suitable for trailer-sailers into locked marina basin during daylight hours: lock gates open for 4 hours either side HW. Refueller (tidal), parking for car and trailer, toilets. Speed limit 6 knots. By arrangement only Tel Medway(0634) 280022. Charge.

Cuxton (River Medway)
Cuxton Marina, Station Road
Leave M 2 at junction 2 following A 228 south. Concrete slipway available for 3 hours either side HW during normal working hours. Diesel, parking for car and trailer (c), toilets, chandlery. Speed limit 6 knots: no water-skiing. Check for availability Tel Medway(0634) 721941. Charge.

Gravesend
Gravesend Canal Basin
Turn off M 2 following signs to Gravesend East, going along Valley Drive into Abbey Rd, turning left into Milton Rd, and right into Ordnance Rd turn left at Canal Rd onto the Promenade and look for the wooden bridge; site is adjacent. Concrete and wooden ramp available at all states of tide and suitable all craft. Petrol, parking for car and trailer in compound (c), crane, toilets and showers (c), chandlery from Miller Marine or Starbucks. Speed limit 3mph: no water-skiing. Further information from the lock master Tel Gravesend(0474) 352392/337489. Charge (licence required) and harbour dues payable.

ESSEX

Pitsea, Vange Creek (Thames Estuary)
Wat Tyler Country Park
Leave A 13 at Pitsea, following Wat Tyler Way to the Country Park. Steep concrete slipway available for 3 hours either side HW from 0900 - dusk and suitable most craft. No fuel, parking for car and trailer, toilets, chandlery from S Gray. Speed limit 8 knots in creek: water-skiing allowed in designated area (1 mile). Further information from Marine Warden Tel Basildon(0268) 552044. Charge.

South Benfleet (Thames Estuary)
Benfleet Causeway
Follow A 13 Southend road, turning off on B 1014: site is at bridge between S Benfleet and Canvey Is. Concrete slipway available for 2 hours either side HW and suitable small craft only. Fuel, limited parking for car, trailers can be left in School Lane car park (¼ mile N of railway station), toilets in School Lane, nearest chandlers in Canvey. Speed limit 8 knots: no water-skiing. No Charge.

Leigh-on-Sea (Thames Estuary)
Two Tree Island
Follow A 13 to Leigh, turning at railway station into Marsh Rd. Concrete slipway available for 4 hours either side HW and suitable all types of craft. Fuel, parking for car and trailer (c), toilets, chandlery from Walkers Yacht Chandlery. Speed limit 8 knots: water-skiing in designated areas. Further information from the Foreshore Office, Pier Hill, Southend-on-Sea Tel Southend(0702) 611889. Charge.

Leigh-on-Sea (Thames Estuary)
Old High Street
Follow A 13 into Leigh Old Town. Concrete slipway available for 2 hours either side HW and suitable dinghies only. Fuel, limited parking for car and trailer, toilets, chandlery from Walkers Yacht Chandlery. Speed limit 8 knots: water-skiing in designated areas. Charge.

Southend-on-Sea (Thames Estuary)
Esplanade
Follow A 13 or A 127 to seafront. Concrete slipway onto sand available for 2 hours either side HW and suitable for dinghies only. Fuel, parking for car and trailer (c), toilets, chandlers nearby. Speed limit 8 knots: water-skiing in designated areas. Charge.

Shoeburyness (Thames Estuary)
West Beach

Follow A 13 about 4 miles east of Southend: site is on seafront opposite the end of Waterford Rd and adjacent Coastguard Station. Steep concrete slipway onto hard sand available for 4 hours either side HW and suitable all types of craft. Fuel, parking for car and trailer (c), toilets, nearest chandlers Thorpe Bay Marine. Speed limit 8 knots: water-skiing permitted in buoyed area with access corridor. Site is administered by Southend Watersports Club Tel Southend(0702) 219351. Charge.

Shoeburyness (Thames Estuary)
East Beach Road

Follow A 13 about 4 miles east of Southend: access is through East Beach car park. Concrete slipway onto hard sand available 2½ hours either side HW. Fuel, parking for car and trailer (c). Speed limit 8 knots: water- skiing in designated area. Charge.

Paglesham (River Roach)
J W Shuttlewood Ltd, East End

Follow B 1013 from A 127 and signs to Paglesham. Concrete slipway available at all states of tide 0800-1830 (May-Sept only) and suitable all craft up to 30'LOA. Diesel, parking for car and trailer (c), toilets, boatyard facilities on site. Speed limit 8 knots in moorings: water-skiing permitted in designated areas. Check for availability Tel Canewdon(037 06) 226. Charge.

River Crouch

A popular east coast yachting centre famous for "Burnham Week". Harbour dues must be paid to the Crouch Harbour Authority, Harbour Office, 22 High St, Burnham-on-Crouch Tel Maldon(0621) 783602 and a licence must be obtained to use the designated ski area. There is a speed limit of 8 knots in certain areas of the river.

Wallasea Island (River Crouch)
Essex Marina, Canewdon

From London follow the A 12/A 127/B 1013 and signs to Canewdon. Concrete slipway available for 4 hours either side HW. Fuel, parking for car and trailer (c), toilets, chandlery. Check for availability Tel Canewdon(037 06) 531. Charge and harbour dues payable.

Hullbridge Ford, Ferry Road (River Crouch)

Follow A 130 from Chelmsford, then local roads: site is on south bank of river. Launching from tarmac road onto shingle for 2 hours either side HW. No fuel, parking for car and trailer, chandlery from village. No Charge but harbour dues payable.

South Woodham Ferrers (River Crouch)

From Chelmsford follow A 130 turning onto B 1012 and follow road past station: site is on north bank of river opposite Hullbridge in Country Park. Launching from poor shingle and mud surface for 2 hours either side HW. No fuel, parking for car and trailer (c sun only), no toilets, nearest chandlers in Hullbridge. No Charge but harbour dues payable.

River Blackwater

A large area of sheltered water ideal for day-sailing and giving access to the Thames Estuary. There is a speed limit of 8 knots within 250m HW mark of much of the southern shore of the river. For further information contact Maldon DC Tel Maldon(0621) 54477.

Bradwell-on-Sea (River Blackwater)
Bradwell Marina, Waterside

From Chelmsford follow A 414 to Maldon, then B 1018/1010/1020 and 1021. Two concrete slipways available at all states of tide except 1½ hours either side LW. Fuel, parking for car and trailer (c), toilets and showers, overnight berths, chandlery. Speed limit 2 knots in marina and 4 knots in Bradwell Ck. Check for availabilty Tel Maldon (0621) 76235/76391. Charge.

St Lawrence Bay (River Blackwater)
The Stone (Ramsey Island)
From Chelmsford follow the A 414 to Maldon, then B 1018/B1010 following signs for Bradwell-on-Sea, turning left after 6 miles to The Stone. Concrete slipway onto hard sand available at all states of tide. Fuel in village, very limited parking for car and trailer, toilets and chandlery from Stone Marine Store. Charge.

Maylandsea (River Blackwater)
Dan, Webb & Feesey Boatyard, Riverside Estate
Follow B 1018 from Maldon towards Bradwell-on-Sea, turning off to Maylandsea. Concrete slipway available for 3 hours either side HW. Fuel, parking for car and trailer (c), toilets, chandlery. By arrangement only Tel Maldon(0621) 740264. Charge.

Maldon (River Blackwater)
Promenade Park
Follow A 414 from Chelmsford: site is adjacent Maldon YC. Steep concrete slipway available from 2 hours before HW to 1 hour after and suitable sailing craft up to 20'LOA (max weight 650 kilos). Cars cannot get on to the slipway and recovery is up a steep slope. No fuel, parking for car and trailer (c), toilets. Speed limit 8 knots: no water-skiing. Further information from River Bailiff Tel Maldon(0621) 54477. No Charge.

Maldon (River Blackwater)
Dan, Webb & Feesey Boatyard, North Street
Follow A 414 from Chelmsford to Hythe Quay. Concrete slipway available for 2 hours either side HW. Fuel, parking for car and trailer (c), toilets, chandlery. By arrangement only Tel Maldon(0621) 54280. Charge.

Maldon (River Blackwater)
North Street Public Hard
Follow A 414 from Chelmsford: site is adjacent Dan, Webb and Feesey boatyard. Small rough hard available for 2 hours either side HW and suitable dinghies only. Fuel, parking for car and trailer in town, chandlers. No Charge.

Tollesbury (River Blackwater)
Woodrolfe Boatyard, Tollesbury Marina
From Maldon follow B 1026 turning off to follow signs. Concrete slipway into Woodrolfe Ck available 2½ hours either side HW. Diesel, parking for car and trailer, toilets, chandlery, crane, boatlift and overnight berths. Speed limit 4 knots in creek, 8 knots in Tollesbury Fleet. Check for availability Tel Maldon(0621) 869202/868471. Charge.

Mersea Island (River Blackwater)
The Strood
Follow the B 1025 from Colchester: site is on the mainland side of the causeway on the east side of the road. Launching over shingle onto soft mud available for approx 2 hours either side HW and suitable dinghies and sailboards only. No facilities and very limited parking as the road floods on spring tides. No Charge.

Launching on the west side of the Strood and use of the designated water-ski area is for members of The Colchester Water Ski Club only.

West Mersea (River Blackwater)
Lifeboat Hard, Coast Road
From Colchester follow the B 1025 to Mersea Island and signs to West Mersea going through the village to the waterfront. Shingle hard available for launching for approx 4 hours either side HW and suitable all craft. Fuel, limited parking for car and trailer, toilets, chandlery from Mersea Marine Supplies. Charge. **Note:** hard and access must be kept clear at all times for lifeboat launching.

Rowhedge (River Colne)
Public Hard
Take A 134 from Colchester town centre, forking right immediately to follow signs: site is adjacent Anchor Inn and access is awkward due to angle of approach. Concrete slipway onto shingle available for 1½ hours either side HW and suitable dinghies only. Fuel, parking for car and trailer. Speed limit 6 knots. Site is owned by Rowhedge Hard Assoc. No Charge.

Alresford (River Colne)
Alresford Creek
Follow A 133 and B 1027 from Colchester turning right into Alresford Village and following road through the village to road marked "Ford". Launching over shingle available 2½ hours either side HW and suitable small craft. No fuel, limited parking for car and trailer, nearest chandlers in Brightlingsea. Speed Limit 8 knots. No Charge.

Brightlingsea (Brightlingsea Creek)
Town Hard
From Colchester follow A 133, B 1027 and B 1029. Hard shingle foreshore available at all states of tide and suitable all types of craft. Fuel, parking for car (c) in Tower St or Oyster Tank Rd, toilets, chandlers. Speed limit 5 knots: water-skiing in designated areas for members of Brightlingsea Power Boat and Water Ski Club only. Charge.

St Osyth (St Osyth Creek)
St Osyth Boatyard
From Colchester follow A 133 and B 1027 turning right in village. Shingle hard available for 1½ hours either side HW. No fuel, parking for car and trailer, toilets and pub. Speed limit in creek: water-skiing in designated area only. No Charge.

St Osyth (St Osyth Creek)
Mill Dam Lake
From Colchester follow A 133 and B 1027 turning off to St Osyth and turning right in village: site is at lake at top of creek. Concrete slipway available at all times by arrangement only Tel St Osyth(0255) 820535 and suitable powerboats only. No fuel, parking for car and trailer, toilets, nearest chandlers in Brightlingsea. Site is for water-skiing only. Charge.

St Osyth
Point Clear Bay (Multitype Marine)
Turn off B 1027 from Clacton following signs to St Osyth and Point Clear. Concrete slipway available at all times but best within 3/4 hours HW and suitable craft up to 18'LOA: tractor assistance available. Fuel, parking for car and trailer (secure parking available (c)), toilets, telephone, chandlery and yard facilities. Site gives access to open sea via Colne Ck and River Colne: speed limit 5 knots in harbour. Further information Tel Clacton(0255) 821032. Charge.

Clacton-on-Sea
Gunfleet Slipway
Follow A 133 to seafront: site is opposite Lyndhurst Rd. Concrete slipway available for 3 hours either side HW suitable dinghies: site is at right angles to road and manoeuvring is difficult. Fuel, parking for car (c), toilets, chandlery from Nucleus Sailboard and Leisure, Frinton Rd. Speed limit 8 knots within 100m of LW mark. No Charge.

Clacton-on-Sea
Marine Parade West
Follow A 133 to seafront: site is ¼ mile south of Pier. Concrete slipway onto hard sand available for 2½ hours either side HW and suitable all craft up to 20'LOA. Fuel in town, parking for car (c), toilets, nearest chandlers Frinton Boat Centre. Speed limit 8 knots inshore: water-skiing permitted offshore. No Charge.

Clacton-on-Sea
Holland Haven
Follow A 133 from Colchester and B 1032: access is from the Esplanade, Kings Cliff: site is adjacent Clacton-on-Sea SC. Concrete slipway onto sand available 3 hours either side HW and suitable dinghies only. No fuel, parking for car and trailer (c), toilets, nearest chandlers Frinton Boat Centre. Speed limit 8 knots inshore: water-skiing permitted offshore. Charge.

Frinton-on-Sea
Frinton Esplanade
Follow A 133 and B 1033 from Colchester to seafront. Concrete slipway onto hard sand available for 3 hours either side HW and suitable all craft. Fuel in town, parking for car and trailer (c), toilets, chandlery from Frinton Boat Centre. Speed limit 8 knots inshore: water- skiing permitted outside limit. Access to site is locked: key from Beach Attendant or Council Offices, Old Road, Frinton. Charge.

Frinton-on-Sea
The Leas
Follow A 133 and B 1033 from Colchester along the Esplanade and Cliff Way. Concrete slipway onto hard sand available at all states of tide and suitable all craft up to 20'LOA. Fuel, parking for car and trailer (c), toilets, chandlery from Frinton Boat Centre. Speed limit 8 knots inshore: water-skiing permitted offshore. No Charge.

Walton-on-the-Naze
Follow A 133 and B 1033/1034 from Colchester to seafront: site is on north side of Pier. Concrete slipway onto hard sand best for 2 hours either side HW and suitable all craft up to 20'LOA. Fuel in town, parking (c) but not for trailer, toilets, chandlery from Frinton Boat Centre. Speed limit 8 knots inshore: water-skiing permitted outside limit. Charge.

Walton-on-the-Naze (Walton Backwaters)
Town Hard
Follow A 133 and B 1033/1034 from Colchester to town centre then turn left off High St into Mill Lane. Shingle foreshore available for 1½ hours either side HW and suitable all craft up to 20'LOA. Fuel, parking for car and trailer (c), toilets nearby, chandlers. Speed limit 8 knots: no water-skiing. No Charge.

Walton-on-the-Naze (Walton Backwaters)
Titchmarsh Marina
From Colchester follow the A 133/B 1033 and B 1034. Concrete slipway available at all states of tide from 0830-1700 daily and suitable dinghies only. Fuel, parking for car and trailer (c), toilets, chandlery from Marine Traders. Speed limit 4 knots: no water-skiing. By arrangement only Tel Frinton(02556) 2185. Charge

Dovercourt
Follow A 120 from Colchester to Harwich, following signs to seafront: site is adjacent Boating Lake. Concrete slipway onto sand available for 2 hours either side HW. Fuel in town, parking for car and trailer (c), toilets. Speed limit 8 knots in harbour: water-skiing allowed in designated area clear of shipping channel. Charge.

Harwich Harbour
Kings Quay Slip, Wellington Road
Follow A 120 from Colchester: access is via King's Quay St and site is adjacent Harwich Town SC. Concrete slipway onto shingle available at all states of tide for small boats or within 3 hours HW for larger craft. Fuel, parking for car and trailer, toilets, chandlery from Kings Head Marine. Speed limit 8 knots: no water-skiing in harbour. This is a busy commercial harbour: keep clear of deep-water channel and ferry terminals. No Charge.

Manningtree (River Stour)
Quay Street
Follow A 137 from Colchester: site is opposite Stour SC. Concrete slipway onto shingle available for 2 hours either side HW. Fuel on Quay, parking for car and trailer (c). Speed limit 8 knots: water-skiing in designated area between Harkstead Pt and Erwarton Ness. No Charge.

SUFFOLK

Brantham (River Stour)
Cattawade Street
Follow A 137 from Colchester, turning right after crossing the river: site is near old bridge. Concrete slipway with rollers and winch available for 1½ hours either side HW for launching into tidal river or at all times for launching into the non-tidal river giving access to Flatford Mill for small boats without masts. Fuel, parking for car and trailer. Speed limit 8 knots: no water-skiing. No Charge.

Shotley Gate
Harwich Harbour
Follow B 1456 from A 137 south of Ipswich to tip of peninsula: site is past pub and Shotley SC at end of road and adjacent Peninsula Boatyard. Concrete slipway onto shingle available for 4 hours either side HW. Fuel in village, parking for car and trailer, toilets, chandlers. Speed limit 8 knots: no water-skiing. Charge.

Shotley Point
Shotley Point Marina
Follow A 137 and B 1456 south from Ipswich following signs to Shotley: follow this road through village and to seafront turning left by the Bristol Arms. Launching for large craft is by boat hoist only. Fuel, parking for car and trailer (c), toilets, chandlers and all facilities on site. Further information Tel Ipswich(0473) 348908. Charge.

River Orwell
The river runs for about nine miles from Harwich to Ipswich. It is busy with commercial traffic for which a channel is kept dredged and buoyed. There is a speed limit of 6 knots and water-skiing is allowed in a designated area just east of Suffolk Yacht Harbour.

Pin Mill (River Orwell)
Foreshore
Follow B 1456 from A 137 south of Ipswich turning off to Pin Mill. Shingle foreshore with very gradual slope available for launching 2/3 hours either side HW most suitable small craft only. Fuel, no parking, toilets, chandlery from Jack Ward & Son, pub. No Charge.

Woolverstone (River Orwell)
Woolverstone Marina
Follow B 1456 from A 137 south of Ipswich for 5 miles: site is on south bank of river 7 miles upstream from Harwich. Concrete slipway available for 2½ hours either side HW or at HW only for large craft. Fuel, parking for car and trailer (c), toilets, showers, chandlery and boatyard facilities on site. Check for availability Tel Woolverstone(0473) 84206/84354. Charge.

Levington (River Orwell)
Suffolk Yacht Harbour
Follow A 45 to Felixstowe, turning off to Levington: site is on north bank of river. Concrete slipway available at all states of tide and suitable craft up to 18'LOA and 2 tons. Fuel, parking for car and trailer (c), toilets, chandlery and boatyard facilities on site. Designated water-ski area close by. Check for availability Tel Nacton(047 388) 465. Charge.

Felixstowe
Seafront, Langer Road
Follow A 45: site is at south end of seafront next to Coastguard station. Concrete slipway onto shingle beach available for 2 hours either side HW. Fuel in town, parking for car and trailer (c), dinghy park, toilets. Speed limit inshore: water-skiing permitted outside limits. Access gate through sea wall is closed 31st Oct-1st May for flood prevention. Charge.

River Deben
The river runs for about nine miles from Felixstowe Ferry at the mouth, where the tide runs very strongly, to Woodbridge. There is a shifting shingle bar at the entrance which is generally well buoyed but should be approached with caution. Speed limit 8 knots: water-skiing in designated areas.

Felixstowe Ferry (River Deben)
Follow A 45 from Ipswich and signs to "Sailing Facilities": site is near Felixstowe Ferry SC and adjacent Felixstowe Ferry Boatyard. Shingle foreshore can be used for launching for 3 hours either side HW. Fuel, parking for car and trailer, toilets, chandlers, pub. Site is under control of East Suffolk Water Ski Club & Association Ltd. Charge.

Waldringfield (River Deben)
Foreshore
Follow A 12 eastwards from Ipswich, turning right at Martlesham Red Lion and following signs: site is on west bank of river adjacent Maybush Inn, 3 miles below Woodbridge. Shingle foreshore is available for 2½ hours either side HW and suitable for launching dinghies. Fuel in village, parking for car and trailer (c), toilets, chandlery and other facilities from Waldringfield Boatyard adjacent. No Charge.

Woodbridge (River Deben)
Robertsons Boatyard, Lime Kiln Quay
Follow signs to Woodbridge from A 12. Concrete slipway available for 2 hours either side HW. Fuel, parking for car and trailer (c), no toilets, chandlery. Check for availability Tel Woodbridge(039 43) 2305. Charge.

Ramsholt Quay (River Deben)
Follow A 12, turning off onto A 1152 to Woodbridge and B 1083 to Bawdsey, turning right for Ramsholt at Shottisham. Launching over shingle foreshore for 4 hours either side HW suitable dinghies only. No facilities but excellent pub and parking. No Charge.

Rivers Ore and Alde
The position of the entrance frequently changes due to shifting sands: the ebb runs very strongly out of the river at springs and in onshore winds the entrance can be difficult.

Orford (River Ore)
Town Quay
Turn off A 12 following B 1078 and B 1084. Concrete slipway available at all states of tide and suitable all types of craft up to 20'LOA. Fuel, parking for car and trailer (c), toilets and chandlery from Old Warehouse Chandlery. Speed limit 5 knots through moorings: water-skiing allowed in designated area by licence only for club members. Contact Quay Warden Tel Orford(039 45) 450713. Charge.

Aldeburgh (River Alde)
R F Upson & Co, Slaughden Quay
From A 12 turn onto A 1094. Concrete slipway onto shingle available at all states of tide until 1700 or later by arrangement. Fuel, parking for car and trailer, toilets, chandlery. Speed limit 6 knots through moorings: water-skiing in designated areas. Check for availability Tel Aldeburgh(072 885) 2896. Charge.

Southwold Harbour (River Blyth)
Harbour Slipway
Turn off A 12 onto A 1095. Concrete slipway available at all states of tide and suitable all craft. Diesel, petrol (1 mile), parking for car and trailer (c overnight), toilets, chandlery and boatyard facilities from Southwold Boatyard. Speed limit 4 knots in harbour, no speed limit in river. For further information contact the Harbour Master Tel Southwold(0502) 723502. No Charge but harbour dues payable.

Southwold
Turn off A 12 onto A 1095, turning left into Pier Ave after Mights Bridge. Concrete slipway available for 3 hours either side HW. Fuel in town, parking for car and trailer (c), toilets. Speed limit 8 knots inshore: water-skiing permitted outside limit. Conditions here can be very exposed and site is closed from Nov to May by flood gates. No Charge.

NORFOLK

Gorleston-on-Sea (River Yare)
Riverside Road
Follow A 12 from Lowestoft and signs to Gorleston Beach: site is on west bank of river. Concrete slipway available for 4 hours either side HW. Fuel, parking for car and trailer, no toilets, chandlery from Gorleston Marine Ltd. Speed limit in river: no water-skiing. Site gives access to Norfolk Broads or open sea; Gt Yarmouth is a busy commercial harbour. No Charge but harbour dues payable.

Hemsby
Beach
Follow A 149 and B 1159 about 6 miles north of Gt Yarmouth. A track leads to a sandy beach where light craft can be launched. No facilities: access and parking can be difficult at peak times. Site suitable for use in settled conditions only. Speed limit 8 knots inshore: water-skiing permitted outside limit. No Charge.

Winterton-on-Sea
Beach
Follow A 149 and B 1159 about 8 miles north of Gt Yarmouth. Follow signs to beach and launch from sandy foreshore. No facilities: access and parking can be difficult at peak times. Site suitable for use in settled conditions only. Speed limit 8 knots inshore: water-skiing permitted outside limit. No Charge.

Whimpwell Green
Cart Gap, Eccles Beach
Follow signs from B 1159. Wooden ramp to soft sand available for 2 hours either side HW and suitable small craft only. No fuel, parking for car and trailer, no toilets. Speed limit 8 knots inshore: water-skiing permitted outside limit. Conditions can be dangerous here. No Charge.

Happisburgh
Turn off B 1159 close to lighthouse: site is adjacent Lifeboat House. Wooden ramp to beach is available for 2 hours either side HW and suitable small craft only. No fuel, limited parking, no toilets. Speed limit 8 knots inshore: water-skiing permitted outside limit. Conditions can be dangerous here. No Charge.

Walcott Gap

Follow signs from B 1159 five miles north east of North Walsham: site is opposite Walcott Caravan Park. Concrete slipway onto sand available for 2 hours either side HW and suitable light craft only. Fuel, parking for car and trailer, toilets. Speed limit 8 knots inshore: water-skiing permitted outside limit. Open sea conditions. No Charge.

Bacton
Beach

Follow B 1150 to coast from North Walsham and signpost to beach from village. Launch from sandy foreshore at end of lane. No facilities, parking for car and trailer 200yds. Site suitable for use in settled conditions only. Speed limit 8 knots inshore: water-skiing permitted outside limit. No Charge.

Mundesley
Beach

Follow B 1145 north east from North Walsham. Launch from sandy beach with ramps from road. No facilities. Site suitable for use in settled conditions only. Speed limit 8 knots inshore: water-skiing permitted outside limit. No Charge.

Overstrand
Beach

Follow B 1159 east from Cromer and signs to beach. Launching over sandy foreshore for light craft only. No facilities. Site suitable for use in settled conditions only. Speed limit 8 knots inshore. No Charge.

Cromer

Follow A 140 north from Norwich: site is adjacent old lifeboat station but cars can only go some of the way and trailer must be manhandled to ramp. Fuel at local garages, parking may be difficult especially at peak times. Site suitable for use in settled conditions only. No Charge.

Cromer
East Runton Gap

Turn off A 149 three miles west of Cromer at East Runton: site is close Gap caravan site. Steep concrete slipway onto shingle available for 2 hours either side HW. No fuel, parking for car and trailer, toilets. Speed limit 8 knots inshore: water-skiing permitted outside limit. Site used by local fishing boats which may block access. No Charge.

Cromer
West Runton

Follow A 149 west from Cromer. Road to foreshore ends in ramp to sandy beach suitable light craft only. Fuel ($\frac{1}{2}$ mile), parking for car and trailer. Site suitable for use in settled conditions only. No Charge.

Blakeney Harbour
Blakeney Quay

Follow signs to Quay off A 149 west of Cromer. Three concrete slipways available for 3 hours either side HW and suitable all craft. Fuel, parking for car and trailer (c), toilets, chandlery and boatyard facilities from Stratton Long Marine, Westgate St. Speed limit 8 knots: water-skiing permitted at west end of harbour. No Charge.

Blakeney Harbour
Morston

Follow yellow "Quay" sign off A 149 west of Blakeney. Shingle foreshore available for launching 3 hours either side HW. No fuel, parking for car and trailer, toilets, chandlery from Stratton Long Marine, Blakeney. Speed limit 8 knots: water-skiing permitted at west end of harbour. No Charge.

Wells-next-the-Sea
East Quay
Turn off A 149 and follow signs to harbour. Concrete slipway with winch and trolley available 3 hours either side HW and suitable craft up to 16'LOA. Fuel, parking for car and trailer (c), toilets, chandlery from Standard House Chandlers. Speed limit 5 knots: water-skiing permitted outside harbour. No Charge but harbour dues payable.

Wells-next-the-Sea
Beach Road
Turn off A 149 and follow signs to harbour: Beach Rd is opposite the caravan site. Launching over shingle foreshore available for 3 hours either side HW suitable for dinghies. Fuel, parking for car and trailer (c), toilets, chandlery from Standard House Chandlers. No Charge.

Burnham Overy Staithe
Turn off A 149: site is opposite Burnham Overy Boathouse and access is via narrow congested road. Steep concrete slipway onto shingle available for 2 hours either side HW and suitable craft up to 18'LOA. No fuel, limited parking (c), no toilets, chandlery from Burnham Overy Boathouse. Speed limit 8 knots. Site can be very congested at peak periods. Charge and harbour dues payable.

Brancaster Harbour
Turn off A 149. There are a number of sites in the harbour where small boats can be launched over shingle for 2/3 hours either side HW. Fuel, parking for car and trailer (c), toilets, chandlery from Brancaster Sailing and Sailboard Centre. Speed limit 6 knots: water-skiing allowed outside limits. The Harbour Master's consent is needed to launch powerboats and sailboarding is restricted. Charge.

Hunstanton
North Beach
Turn off A 149: site is adjacent Pier and SC. Concrete slipway onto hard sand available at most states of tide but best for 2/3 hours either side HW. Fuel, parking for car and trailer (c), toilets. Site is for dinghy sailing and sailboarding only. No Charge.

Hunstanton
South Beach Road (Hunstanton Water Sports Club)
Turn off A 149 at water tower; follow road down hill and straight over at roundabout, turning left at next bend and site is $\frac{1}{2}$ mile on right. Concrete slipway onto sand available at all states of tide and suitable all craft up to 20'LOA. Fuel (1 mile), toilets, chandlers at Brancaster (5 miles). Site is mainly used by Hunstanton Water Sports Club who lease the car park. The club has excellent facilities and welcomes visitors and will assist launching and recovery (c) provided boat owners have proof of insurance and standard safety equipment on board. Speed limit 7 knots within 200m HW mark. Further information from Club Sec Tel Peterborough(0733) 210008. No Charge.

Hunstanton
Heacham Beach North
Turn off A 149 following signs. Steep concrete slipway onto hard sand available for 2/3 hours either side HW and suitable craft up to 20' LOA. No fuel, parking for car and trailer (c), toilets. No speed limit: water-skiing allowed. Further information from Seafront Manager Tel Hunstanton(04853) 2610. No Charge.

King's Lynn (Great Ouse)
Common Staithe Quay
Follow A 10 north to Kings Lynn. Concrete slipway available for 2 hours either side HW and suitable all craft. Fuel, parking for car and trailer (c), toilets, chandlery from Shipshape at Austin Fields. At LW thick mud is exposed. No Charge.

64

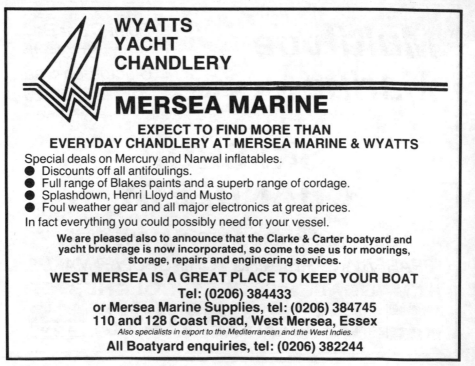

67

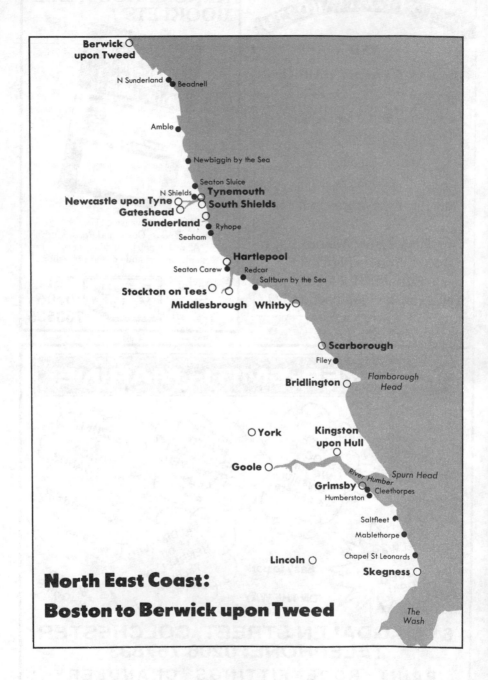

Berwick O
upon Tweed

N Sunderland ● ● Beadnell

Amble ●

Newbiggin by the Sea ●

Seaton Sluice
N Shields **Tynemouth**
Newcastle upon Tyne O ● **South Shields**
Gateshead O
Sunderland ● Ryhope
Seaham ●

Hartlepool
Seaton Carew ● Redcar
Saltburn by the Sea ●
Stockton on Tees O
Middlesbrough **Whitby** O

O **Scarborough**
Filey ●

*Flamborough
Head*

Bridlington O

O **York**   **Kingston
upon Hull**
O

Goole O   *River Humber*   *Spurn Head*

Grimsby O ● Cleethorpes
Humberston ●

Saltfleet ●
Mablethorpe ●

Lincoln O   Chapel St Leonards ●

Skegness O

North East Coast:
Boston to Berwick upon Tweed

*The
Wash*

LINCOLNSHIRE

Skegness
Princes Parade
Follow A 158 east from Lincoln. Launch over sand at any state of tide with assistance of tractor; suitable craft up to 20'LOA. Site is controlled by Skegness Boating Club. Charge.

Skegness
Gibralter Point
Follow A 158 east from Lincoln and minor road 3 miles south from town centre. Site is controlled by Skegness SC; contact the Secretary, Mr S Mason, 18 North Lane, Navenby, Lincoln. Charge.

Ingoldmells
Jacksons Corner
Follow A 52 north from Skegness. Launching over sand at any state of tide with assistance of tractor suitable light craft only. Site is controlled by Skegness SC: contact Secretary as above. Charge.

Chapel St Leonards
Beach
Follow A 52 and minor roads approx 6 miles north from Skegness. Launching over sandy beach from central pullover suitable light craft which can be manhandled only. No Charge.

Sandilands
Sea Lane Pullover
Follow A 52 and minor roads north from Skegness. Launching over sandy beach from Sea Lane pullover suitable light craft which can be manhandled. No Charge.

Sutton-on-Sea
Church Lane Pullover
Follow A 52 north from Skegness. Launching over sandy beach from Church Lane pullover suitable light craft which can be manhandled. No Charge.

Mablethorpe
Seaholme Road Pullover
Follow A 52 north from Skegness. Launching over sandy beach from Seaholme Road pullover suitable light craft which can be manhandled. No Charge.

Saltfleet
Saltfleet Haven
Follow A 1031 south from Cleethorpes; launching available 2 hours either side HW suitable craft up to 25'LOA. Site is controlled by Saltfleet Haven Boat Club: contact the Hon Secretary, D A Pitt, Hove-to, Main Road, Saltfleetby, Nr Louth, Lincs.

HUMBERSIDE

Humberston
Humber Mouth Yacht Club
Follow A 46 and A 1031 from Lincoln. Concrete slipway available 1½ hours either side HW. No fuel, parking for car and trailer (c), toilets. Speed limit 8 knots inshore: water-skiing permitted outside limit. Contact the Secretary, Caravella, 2 Walk Lane, Humberston for permission to use. Charge.

Cleethorpes
Follow A 46 from Lincoln or M 180/A 180: site is next to Pier at end of Sea Road. Concrete slipway onto shingle available for 2 hours either side HW. Fuel from nearby garage, parking for car and trailer (c), toilets, chandlery from Ron Nicholson, 34 Bank St. No speed limit: water-skiing allowed. No Charge.

Cleethorpes
Brighton Street Slipway
Follow A 46 from Lincoln or M 180/A 180: site is on seafront opposite Brighton St.
Slipway of cobbles and concrete available for 2 hours either side HW and suitable craft
which can be manhandled. Fuel from local garage, parking for car and trailer (c), toilets
nearby, chandlery from Ron Nicholson, 34 Bank St. Speed limit 7 knots within 200m of
shore: water-skiing in designated area with access channel. No Charge.

Barrow Haven (River Humber)
Barrow Haven Marina
Turn off A 15 at Barton-on-Humber on south bank of river taking A 1077 east and follow
signs. Concrete slipway available for 4 hours either side HW during working hours and
suitable all craft. Fuel, parking for car, leave trailer by arrangement (c) only. Charge.

Goole (River Humber)
Smith Bros (Goole) Ltd Marina
Follow M 62 east from M 18 to Goole. Concrete slipway available during working hours
and suitable all craft. Diesel, parking for car and trailer (c), toilets, boatyard facilities.
Site also gives access to River Ouse and Inland Waterways. Check for availability Tel
Goole(0405) 763985. Charge.

Kingston-upon-Hull (River Humber)
Hessle Beach
Leave M 180 at junction 5 taking A 15 over Humber Bridge: site is just downstream of
bridge. Launching over stone and shingle foreshore available for 3 hours either side HW
and suitable light craft. No Charge.

Kingston-upon-Hull (River Humber)
Horsewash Slope
Leave M 180 at junction 5 taking A 15 over Humber Bridge: site is just east of Humber
Marina. Launch from stone slope which may be blocked by shipping lying alongside: site
available near HW and suitable light craft which can be manhandled only. No Charge.

Bridlington
South Cliff Slipway
Follow A 166 from York or A 165 from Hull: access is via Belvedere Parade. Concrete
slipway onto hard sand available from 0800 to 1 hour before sunset 1st Apr-31st Oct.
Fuel (1 mile), parking for car (c) and trailer, toilets and showers, chandlers in town, boat
park. Speed limit 8 knots within 300m LWS mark: water-skiing in designated areas. All
boats are inspected before being permitted to launch and local regulations concerning
insurance and safety equipment must be complied with. Charge.

NORTH YORKSHIRE

Filey
Filey Coble Landing
Follow A 64 and A 1039 from York: site is at north end of sea front. Slipway of concrete
and stone setts onto sand available at all states of tide but best 2 hours either side HW
for larger craft. No fuel, parking for car and trailer, toilets. Site for boats with max
engine capacity 20 HP: water-skiing prohibited. Charge.

Scarborough Harbour
Harbour Slipway
Follow A 64 from York: access is via a roadside barrier. Concrete slipway with stone
setts available for 2½ hours either side HW. Fuel, parking for car and trailer (1½ mile):
trailers must be removed from slipway, toilets, chandlers, temporary berths available.
Site for boats with max engine capacity 20 HP: no water-skiing. Charge.

Whitby Harbour
Marina Slipway, Boghall
Follow A 171 east from Middlesbrough or A 64/A 169 from York: site is on west side
upper harbour. Concrete slipway available for 4 hours either side HW and suitable all
craft. Fuel, parking for car and trailer (c), toilets, chandlery, travel hoist and mast hoist
from M R Coates Marine. Slow speed: no water-skiing in harbour but allowed ¼ mile
offshore. Further information Tel Whitby(0947) 600165. Charge. There are two unmade
slips on the east side of the harbour available for 2 hours either side HW: no parking
facilities. Free.

CLEVELAND

Saltburn-by-the-Sea
Seafront
Follow A 174 from Whitby or Middlesbrough: site is near Pier. Launching over shingle
and firm sand for 2/3 hours either side HW and suitable dinghies only. Fuel in village,
parking for car and trailer (c), toilets. Exposed sea conditions in onshore winds. No
Charge.

Redcar
Follow A 1085 from Middlesbrough. Three wide concrete slips along seafront onto firm
sand are available at all states of tide but best for 2/3 hours either side HW and suitable
smaller boats. Fuel in town, parking for car and trailer (c), toilets. Exposed sea conditions
in onshore winds: local knowledge is necessary. No Charge.

River Tees
**All craft using the river must first register with the Harbour Office, Tees Dock,
Grangetown, Tel Middlesbrough(0642) 452541, and sign a form of indemnity.
This is a busy commercial river; take care not to obstruct shipping.**

South Gare, Redcar
South Gare Marine Club
Follow A 1085 from Middlesbrough to Coatham taking "Sea Front" road at traffic lights
by Cowies Garage and turning left at roundabout: the club will be seen on the left after
3 miles: access is via single track private road with passing places. Concrete slipway with
winch and snatch block available at all states of tide except for 1 hour either side LWS
and suitable all craft. No fuel, parking for car and trailer (c), toilets. No speed limit:
water-skiing permitted in designated areas outside river entrance. Further information Tel
Redcar(0642) 482015. Tides may be strong at the river mouth. Charge and harbour dues
payable.

Stockton-on-Tees (River Tees)
Corporation Quay
Follow A 1 (M) north turning off onto A 66 and following signs to Stockton: access is via
the car park in Riverside Road. Concrete slipway available from 3 hours before HW to
about 1 hour after: launching later than this is risky due to strength of ebb tide. Petrol,
parking for car and trailer, no toilets. No speed limit: water-skiing permitted in
designated area 2 miles upstream at Horseshoe Bend. No Charge but harbour dues
payable.

Seaton Carew
Seafront
Follow A 19 from Teesside, then A 689 and B 1276 to seafront. Concrete slipway with
gradual slope onto soft sand available for 2/3 hours either side HW and suitable small
craft only. No fuel, parking for car and trailer (c), no toilets. No speed limit: water-skiing
permitted. Exposed sea conditions in onshore winds: local knowledge is necessary. No
Charge.

71

Hartlepool
Harbour Slipway

Follow A 19 from Teesside then A 689 into Hartlepool and follow signs to Middleton Harbour: site is on north side. Concrete slipway onto shingle and hard sand available for 2 hours either side HW or at all times for smaller craft which can be manhandled across beach. Fuel, parking for car and trailer, toilets, chandlery from Cliff Reynolds Ltd, Whitby St. Speed limit 7 knots in harbour: no water-skiing. No Charge.

Hartlepool
Hartlepool Yacht Club

Follow A 19 and A 689 from Teesside and signs to Middleton Harbour: site is on west side of harbour entrance. Concrete slipway available at all states of tide. Fuel in town, parking for car and trailer, toilets in club, chandlery from Cliff Reynolds, Whitby St. Speed limit 7 knots in harbour: no water-skiing. Further information Tel Hartlepool(0429) 74931. Charge.

Hartlepool
Tees SC

Follow A 19 from Teesside and A 689 to Hartlepool and follow signs to Middleton Harbour: site is over level crossing at end of Church St on south side of basin. Concrete slipway available for 4/5 hours either side HW and suitable craft up to 5 tons. Fuel, parking for car and trailer (c), toilets, chandlery from Cliff Reynolds, Whitby St. Site is available during the season and during club hours (Wed pm and all day Sat and Sun). Further information from the Secretary Tel Hartlepool(0429) 267151. Speed limit 7 knots in harbour: no water-skiing. This is a good sheltered site although the coast here is exposed. No Charge.

Hartlepool
Crimdon Caravan Park

Follow A 1086 from Hartlepool north for 3 miles. Launching from concrete over steeply sloping soft sand onto firmer sand requires use of landrover or similar. Fuel, parking for car and trailer (c), toilets. Advise site office of intention to launch. No Charge.

Seaham Harbour
Harbour Slipway

Follow A 19 north from Middlesbrough, turning off onto B 1285. Steep concrete slipway available for 2 hours either side HW and suitable craft up to 24'LOA and 5' draught. Fuel, parking for car and trailer. Speed limit 5 knots. Charge.

TYNE AND WEAR

Ryhope
Beach

Follow A 19 from Middlesbrough turning onto A 1018. Short narrow concrete slipway onto rocky beach available at HW and suitable small craft only. No fuel, parking for car and trailer, no toilets. Exposed conditions in onshore winds. No Charge.

Hendon
Foreshore

Follow A 1(M) and A 690 to Sunderland: site is south of town. Two short concrete slipways onto rocky beach available for 1 hour either side HW and suitable small craft only. Fuel in town, parking for car and trailer (c), toilets in town. Exposed conditions in onshore winds. No Charge.

River Wear
This is a busy commercial river with a speed limit of 6 knots: water-skiing is not permitted in the river. Access to the sea from the upper reaches is limited to 3 hours either side HW by a barrier. Harbour dues are payable.

Sunderland (River Wear)
Claxheugh Rock
Follow A 690 from A 1(M) to Sunderland: site is on south bank of river 4 miles from mouth. Concrete slipway available for 3 hours either side HW and suitable craft up to 20'LOA. No fuel, parking for car and trailer, no toilets. Charge and harbour dues payable.

Port of Sunderland (River Wear)
South Hylton
Leave A 1(M) taking A 183, and turning off to South Hylton: site is on south bank of river 5 miles from mouth and adjacent to Golden Lion pub. Steep concrete slipway available for 3 hours either side HW and suitable craft up to 20'LOA. Fuel from nearby garage, parking for car and trailer, no toilets. Charge and harbour dues payable.

Port of Sunderland (River Wear)
Fatfield
Turn off A 1(M) south of the Washington Services: site is on north bank of river 9 miles from mouth and access is opposite Fatfield Club. Concrete slipway available for 2½ hours either side HW and suitable craft up to 20'LOA. No fuel, parking for car and trailer, no toilets. Charge and harbour dues payable.

Port of Sunderland (River Wear)
Sir James Steel Park
Turn off A 1(M) south of the Washington Services: site is on the north bank, ten miles from the river mouth. Concrete slipway available for launching 2 hours either side HW. No fuel, parking for car and trailer, toilets. Charge and harbour dues payable.

Roker
Roker Blockyard, Marine Walk
Take A 183 north from town centre: where Harbour View joins Roker Terrace take Pier View Rd to Marine Walk near Bungalow Cafe. Concrete ramp leads from promenade onto soft sandy beach and is available at all states of tide although at LW the water is some distance away: site is suitable for dinghies and small powerboats only. Fuel, parking for car and trailer (c), toilets. Speed limit 6mph. **Note:** Inshore lifeboat launches from this ramp which must be kept clear at all times. Inshore Superintendent's Office is on Marine Walk. Charge.

Whitburn
Beach
Follow A 183 north from Sunderland: a narrow road behind the garage leads to a rocky beach by the boundary mark. Launching over beach suitable light craft only. This is an exposed site in onshore winds. No Charge.

River Tyne
A busy commercial river. All boats are subject to a minimum conservancy charge by the Port of Tyne Authority. There is a speed limit of 6mph on the river and all waterborne activities are subject to the Authority's byelaws.

South Shields (River Tyne)
Follow A 1 and A 194: site is on south bank of the River Tyne estuary. Concrete slipway available at all times except for 1 hour either side LWS and suitable dinghies and power craft. Fuel from local garages, limited parking for car and trailer(c) which becomes very crowded, toilets, chandlers. Site is licence controlled. Charge.

Walker Riverside Park, Newcastle (River Tyne)

Take A 186 Walker road to Walker Pottery Bank and Riverside Park: access is via a steep, winding road from Pottery Bank car park. Fairly steep concrete slipway available during daylight hours for approx 2 hours either side HW and suitable dinghies and trailer sailers. Fuel (1 mile), parking for car and trailer (not overnight), toilets and telephone. Check for availability Tel Tyneside(091) 265 5116. No Charge.

Gateshead (River Tyne)
Friar's Goose Water Sports Club, Green Lane, Felling

Follow A 6127 from A 1(M) into Gateshead: site is on south side of river. Concrete slipway available for 2/3 hours either side HW. Fuel from local garage, parking for car and trailer, toilets at clubhouse, moorings. Further information Tel Tyneside(091) 4692545. Charge.

Derwenthaugh Marina (River Tyne)

Follow signs from the A 69: site is on south bank of river at the confluence of the Rivers Tyne and Derwent near Blaydon and the Scotswood Bridge. Concrete slipway available for 5 hours either side HW and suitable craft up to 35'LOA approx. Fuel, parking for car and trailer, toilets, telephone and chandlers nearby. Speed limit 6mph: fast water zone $\frac{1}{4}$ mile downstream. Site is administered by the Water Sports Assoc: all craft launching here must have 3rd party insurance. Charge.

Tyne Riverside Country Park, Newburn (River Tyne)

Take A 6085 Newcastle to Newburn road, turning off in Newburn into Grange Rd and following signs. Fairly steep concrete slipway available for approx 2 hours either side HW and suitable small craft only. Fuel ($\frac{1}{2}$ mile), parking for car and trailer (not overnight), toilets and telephone. Site is available to members of the Newburn Waterski Club or to owners of small craft by prior arrangement with the Newburn Riverside Recreation Assoc Grange Rd, Newburn, Newcastle NE15. Charge.

North Shields (River Tyne)
Jim Marine, New Quay

Follow A 1058 from Newcastle-upon-Tyne: site is adjacent to North Shields ferry landing. Concrete slipway available 3/4 hours either side HW. Fuel nearby, parking for car and trailer, toilets, showers, chandlery, boat park on site. Further information Tel N Shields(0632) 577610. Charge.

Cullercoats
Harbour Slip

Follow A 1058 east from Newcastle-upon-Tyne to Cullercoats. Concrete slipway into harbour available for 2/3 hours either side HW. Fuel, limited parking for car and trailer, toilets. Speed limit inshore: water-skiing not allowed. Site may be congested at peak times. No Charge.

NORTHUMBERLAND

Seaton Sluice Harbour

Turn off A 1 onto A 190. Two concrete slipways available for 2 hours either side HW. Fuel, parking for car and trailer, toilets. Speed limit 5 mph in harbour and fairway: no water-skiing. Permission to launch must be obtained from Blyth Valley Council at Foreshore and Harbour Office, Links Rd, Blyth Tel(0670) 352269. Charge.

Newbiggin-by-the-Sea
Promenade

Follow A 197 to coast from A 1 at Morpeth. Concrete slipway from Promenade onto hard sand available at all states of tide. Fuel from local garage, parking for car and trailer, toilets. Charge.

Amble (River Coquet Estuary)
The Braid
Follow A 1068 north towards Alnwick, turning off between Amble and Warkworth. Concrete slipway available for 2/3 hours either side HW and suitable all craft. Fuel, parking for car and trailer, toilets, telephone: chandlery and yard facilities from Camper and Nicholson's Marina adjacent. No Charge.

Beadnell
Follow B 1340 north from Alnwick. Small wooden slipway adjacent to car park available for 2/3 hours either side HW and suitable dinghies only. Fuel from local garage, parking for car and trailer (c), toilets nearby. Speed limit 8 knots: water-skiing allowed offshore. Launching is controlled by car park attendant. No Charge.

North Sunderland (Seahouses)
Harbour Slipway
Follow B 1340 north from Alnwick. Concrete slipway onto sand available for 2/3 hours either side HW. Fuel from local garage, parking for car and trailer, toilets nearby. Charge.

Berwick-upon-Tweed
West End Rd, Tweedmouth
Turn off the A 1: site is adjacent old bridge on the south side of the River Tweed. Concrete slipway onto shingle available for 2½ hours either side HW. Fuel from local garage, parking for car and trailer on roadside only, toilets. Speed limit 6 knots. No Charge but harbour dues payable.

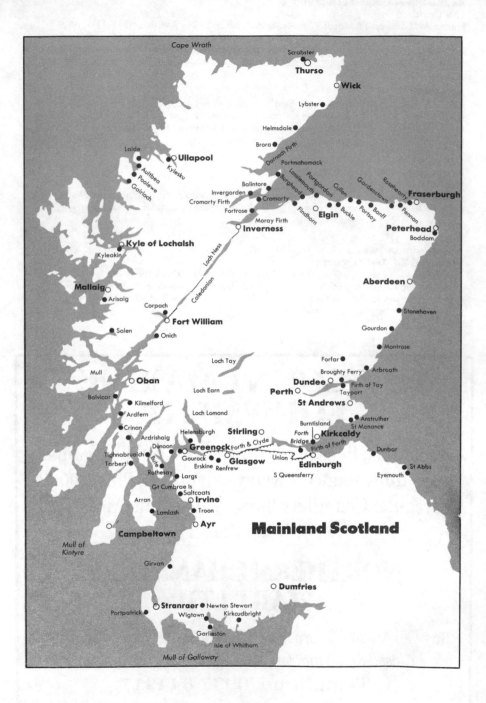

Cape Wrath

Scrabster
Thurso
○ **Wick**
Lybster

Helmsdale
Brora
Dornoch Firth
Portmahomack
Laide ○ **Ullapool**
Aultbea   Kylesku
Poolewe   Balintore   Lossiemouth   Portgordon   Cullen   Gardenstown   Rosehearty
Gairloch   Invergordon   Burghsead   Cromarty   Findhorn   Elgin   Buckie   Portsoy   Banff   Pennan   **Fraserburgh**
Cromarty Firth   Cromarty
Fortrose
Moray Firth   Findhorn   ○ **Elgin**   Buckie
Kyle of Lochalsh   **Inverness**   **Peterhead**
Kyleakin   Boddam

Mallaig○   Loch Ness
Arisaig
Corpach   Caledonian   **Aberdeen** ○
Salen   Stonehaven
Fort William   Gourdon
Onich   Montrose

Loch Tay
Forfar   Arbroath
Broughty Ferry
Mull   Loch Earn   **Dundee** ○   Firth of Tay
○ **Oban**   **Perth** ○   Tayport
Balvicar   **St Andrews** ○
Kilmelford   Loch Lomond
Ardfern   Anstruther
Crinan   St Monance
Ardrishaig   Helensburgh   **Stirling** ○   Burntisland   **Kirkcaldy**
Dunoon   Forth   Forth & Clyde   Bridge
Tighnabruaich   Bute   **Greenock**   Union   Firth of Forth   Dunbar
Tarbert   Gourock   **Glasgow**   S Queensferry   St Abbs
Erskine   Renfrew   **Edinburgh**   Eyemouth
Rothesay   Largs
Gt Cumbrae Is
Arran   Saltcoats
Lamlash   ○ **Irvine**   **Mainland Scotland**
Troon
○   ○ **Ayr**
Campbeltown
Mull of
Kintyre
Girvan

○ **Dumfries**

Portpatrick   **Stranraer** ● Newton Stewart
Wigtown   Kirkcudbright
Garlieston
Isle of Whithorn
Mull of Galloway

BORDERS

Eyemouth Harbour
Harbour Slipway
Follow A 1 north from Berwick-upon-Tweed, taking the A 1107 to Eyemouth. Concrete slipway north of the pier but with limited access available for 3/4 hours either side HW and suitable dinghies and powerboats. Fuel, parking for car and trailer, toilets, chandlers. Speed limit 5 mph in harbour: water-skiing permitted offshore. This is a busy fishing harbour which can be very congested: there is a free slipway on the beach. Charge and harbour dues payable.

St Abbs Harbour
Harbour Slipway
Follow A 1 north from Berwick-upon-Tweed, taking A 1107 and B 6438 at Coldingham: final approach to harbour is steep and narrow. Concrete slipway available for 3/4 hours either side HW for larger craft: smaller craft can be manhandled across hard sand at LW. Fuel from garage at Coldingham (1½ miles), parking for car and trailer, toilets, nearest chandlers in Eyemouth (5 miles). Speed limit in harbour: water-skiing permitted outside harbour. This is a popular and busy site in offshore winds: there is no launching in onshore winds when the site is very exposed. For advice contact the Harbour Master. Charge.

LOTHIAN

Dunbar Harbour
Harbour Slipway
Follow A 1 north from Berwick-upon-Tweed taking A 1087 to Dunbar: site is at end of main street. Slipway of stone pitching onto level rock and sand available for 3/4 hours either side HW. Fuel from local garages, parking for car, leave trailer by arrangement with Harbour Master, toilets in High St, nearest chandlers in Eyemouth. Site is rocky and exposed and unsuitable for water-skiing. Charge.

Fisherrow Harbour (Firth of Forth)
Harbour Slipway, New Street
Follow A 1 east from Edinburgh to Musselburgh. Slipway of stone pitching available for 3 hours either side HW. Fuel from garage, parking for car and trailer, toilets in South St. Speed limit 3 knots in harbour: water-skiing allowed outside harbour (further information from Musselburgh Water-Ski Club: contact Mrs Margaret Wayth Tel Edinburgh(031) 665 5414). Charge.

Newhaven Harbour (Firth of Forth)
Harbour Slipway
Leave M 8 at junction 2 taking A 8 to Edinburgh city centre then follow signs to Newhaven. Cobbled slipway available for 4 hours either side HW and suitable all craft. Permission to launch must be obtained in advance from the Forth Ports Authority, Tower Place, Leith Tel Edinburgh(031) 554 4343. Fuel nearby, limited parking in adjacent roads, toilets. Charge.

Granton Harbour (Firth of Forth)
Harbour Slipway
Leave M 8 at junction 2, taking A 8 to Edinburgh city centre then follow signs to Granton: site is on east side Middle Pier. Cobbled slipway available for 4 hours either side HW and suitable all craft although trailers must be manhandled. A permit must be obtained in advance from Forth Ports Authority, Tower Place, Leith Tel Edinburgh(031) 554 4343 and permission to launch must be obtained from the Piermaster at the end of the Quay. Fuel nearby, parking for car and trailer by arrangement, toilets, chandlery. Charge and harbour dues payable.

Cramond (Firth of Forth)
Riverside Walk Slipway
Leave M 8 at junction 2, taking A 8/A 902 and minor roads to Cramond: site is at mouth of river on east bank. Concrete slipway available for 2 hours either side HW and suitable craft up to 25'LOA. No fuel, parking for car and trailer in nearby car park (c), toilets. No speed limit: water-skiing allowed. Cramond Boat Club is adjacent Tel Edinburgh (031) 336 1356. Charge.

South Queensferry (Firth of Forth)
Port Edgar Marina
Leave M 8 at junction 1 taking A 8000 and minor roads: site is just west of Forth Bridge. Concrete slipway available for 5 hours either side HW 0830-2200: other times by arrangement. Diesel on site, petrol (1 mile), parking for car and trailer, toilets, chandlery and other facilities. Speed limit 3 knots in harbour: water-skiing permitted in designated area downstream. Further information Tel Edinburgh(031) 331 3330. Charge.

FIFE

North Queensferry (Firth of Forth)
Forth Yacht Marina
Follow signs to Nth Queensferry after crossing Forth Br: site is between road and rail bridges. Concrete slipway available for 3/4 hours either side HW. Diesel on site, petrol (1 mile), parking for car and trailer, toilets, chandlery, crane. No speed limit: water-skiing permitted in designated area downstream. Charge.

Aberdour (Firth of Forth)
Shore Road Slipway
Follow A 92 east from the north side of the Forth Bridge: site is at pier. Concrete slipway onto beach available for 2 hours either side HW suitable craft up to 20'LOA. Fuel, parking for car and trailer. No Charge.

Burntisland (Firth of Forth)
Burntisland Beach
From north side of the Forth Br follow A 92 east. Concrete slipway onto beach available at all states of tide for small boats. Fuel (150yds), parking for car and trailer, toilets, chandlery from Lammerlaws Leisure Water Sports Shop (50yds). No speed limit: water-skiing permitted. No Charge.

Burntisland Harbour (Firth of Forth)
Outer Harbour Slipway
From north side of the Forth Br follow A 92 east. Concrete slipway available at all states of tide. Fuel from garage, parking for car and trailer, toilets nearby, chandlers. Further information from the Harbour Master Tel Leven(0333) 26725. Charge.

Kinghorn (Firth of Forth)
Longboat Inn, Pettycur Road
Follow A 92 east from north side of the Forth Br. Concrete slipway and crane available at all states of tide except for 1 hour either side LWS. Diesel on site, petrol ($\frac{1}{2}$ mile), parking for car and trailer (c for visitors), toilets, nearest chandlers ($2\frac{1}{2}$ miles). No speed limit: water-skiing allowed. Charge.

St Monance (Firth of Forth)
Harbour Slipway
Follow A 917 south from St Andrews. Concrete slipway by root of east pier and close Harbour Masters' Office available for 3 hours either side HW. Fuel from garage, parking for car and trailer. Speed limit in harbour: water-skiing allowed offshore. Charge.

Anstruther Harbour (Firth of Forth)
Harbour Slipway
Follow A 917 south from St Andrews. Concrete slipway available for 3 hours either side HW and suitable all craft up to 35'LOA. Diesel, parking for car and trailer (c), toilets, crane, chandlery from Anster Chandlers, Shore St. Speed limit 3 knots in harbour: water-skiing allowed offshore. Further information from the Harbour Master Tel Anstruther (0333) 310836. Charge and harbour dues payable.

Cellardyke Harbour (Firth of Forth)
Harbour Slipway
Site is 1 mile east of Anstruther. Concrete slipway available for 3 hours either side HW. Fuel from Anstruther, parking for car and trailer, toilets. Speed limit 3 knots in harbour: water-skiing allowed outside. Further information from the Harbour Master Tel Anstruther(0333) 310836. Charge.

St Andrews Harbour
Harbour Slipway
Leave M 90 at junction 7 taking the A 91 east: site is in corner of outer harbour. Concrete slipway available for 2 hours either side HW. Fuel ($\frac{1}{2}$ mile), parking for car and trailer. Obtain Harbour Master's permission before launching. Slow speed in harbour: water-skiing allowed outside. Charge.

Tayport (Firth of Tay)
Harbour Slipway (Tayport Boat Owners Assoc)
Leave M 90 at junction 8 following A 91 and A 914, then B 946. Slipway of concrete and cobbles available for 3 hours either side HW and suitable all craft. Petrol, parking for car and trailer(c), toilets, chandlery from Scots Craig. Speed limit 5mph in harbour: water-skiing allowed offshore. Charge and harbour dues payable.

TAYSIDE

Perth (River Tay)
Tay Street, Railway Bridge
Follow M 90 north to Perth and signs to town centre. Granite sett slipway available at all states of tide and suitable dinghies and powerboats. Fuel, parking for car, toilets, chandlery. Speed limit: water-skiing allowed in designated area. No Charge.

Perth (River Tay)
Perth Water Ski Club
Leave M 90 at junction 10 following signs to town centre: site is in Shore Rd. Concrete slipway available for 2 hours either side HW and suitable all craft up to 25'LOA. Fuel, parking for car and trailer (c), chandlery. No speed limit: water-skiing permitted. Insurance certificate must be shown. Charge.

Broughty Ferry (Firth of Tay)
Harbour Slipway
Follow A 930 east from Dundee town centre for 3 miles. Concrete slipway available for 4/5 hours either side HW suitable for dinghies. Speed limit 5 knots inshore with access lane from slip to designated watersport area. No Charge.

Broughty Ferry (Firth of Tay)
East Coast Watersports Co Ltd
Follow A 930 east from Dundee town centre for 3 miles: site is just east of Broughty Castle. Cobblestone slipway available for 3 hours either side HW and suitable all craft up to 25'LOA. Fuel, parking for car and trailer, toilets and showers, nearest chandlers (1 mile). Speed limit 5 knots inshore with access lanes to designated watersports area. Further information Tel Dundee(0382) 827161/79889. No Charge.

GRAMPIAN

Inverbervie
Gourdon Harbour

Follow A 92 from Dundee and signs: site is south of Inverbervie. Two steep concrete slipways onto soft mud available for 1½ hours either side HW and suitable craft up to 25'LOA. Fuel (diesel only from local Fishermans Soc), parking for car and trailer in car park at West Pier, toilets, some chandlery from Gourdon Fishermans Assoc, repairs from J Craig. Slow speed in harbour: site unsuitable for water-skiing. This is a commercial fishing harbour giving access to an exposed and rocky coastline. Contact Harbour Master, 4 Shoretrack Court, Tel Inverbervie(0561) 61779 for advice and permission to launch. Charge.

Stonehaven
Harbour Slipway

Follow A 92 south from Aberdeen and signs to harbour along High St, turning south past YC to southern corner of harbour. Two concrete slipways onto hard sand available for 4 hours either side HW and suitable dinghies and light craft. Fuel nearby, parking for car and trailer, toilets. Speed limit 3mph: water-skiing outside harbour. Contact Harbour Master Tel (0569) 52571. Charge.

Boddam Harbour
Harbour Slipway

Turn off A 952 south of Peterhead. Concrete slipway available at all states of tide and suitable all craft. Petrol, parking for car only, toilets. Further information from Mr James Barclay Tel Peterhead(0779) 73408. Charge.

Peterhead
The Lido

Follow A 92 and A 952 north from Aberdeen and B 9108: site is adjacent caravan site. Launching over firm sand available at all states of tide suitable for dinghies and powerboats. Fuel, parking for car and trailer, toilets. Water-skiing permitted offshore. No Charge.

Fraserburgh
Balaclava Inner Harbour

Follow A 92, 42 miles north from Aberdeen and signs from town centre. Concrete slipway available for 3 hours either side HW and suitable all craft up to 25'LOA. Fuel, parking for car and trailer, crane for hire, chandlers in Shore St. Speed dead slow in harbour: water-skiing allowed in Fraserburgh Bay. This is a busy fishing and commercial port and is not ideal for pleasure craft. No Charge but harbour dues payable.

Rosehearty (Moray Firth)
Harbour Slipway

Follow B 9031 off the A 98 west of Fraerburgh: site is 4 miles west of Fraserburgh. Fairly steep concrete slipway onto firm sand available at all states of tide or for 2 hours either side HW for larger craft and suitable craft up to 25'LOA. Fuel, parking for car and trailer in Shore St, toilets, boatyard at Sandhaven. Water-skiing allowed offshore in sheltered waters of Port Rae. Further information contact Harbour Master, Mr Ian Downie, 26 Brucklay St Tel Rosehearty(034 67) 292. Charge.

Pennan Harbour (Moray Firth)
Harbour Slipway

Follow B 9031, 10½ miles west from Fraserburgh: access to harbour is via steep road. Gentle concrete slipway onto sand and shingle available for 2 hours either side HW and suitable dinghies and powerboats. No fuel, very limited parking for car and trailer, toilets. Site is very exposed especially in northerly winds. No Charge.

Gardenstown Harbour (Moray Firth)
Gardenstown Slipway
From Fraserburgh follow A 98 and B 9032/9031 west. Steep concrete slipway available for 2 hours either side HW. Diesel on site, petrol in village, parking for car and trailer, toilets. Speed limit: water-skiing allowed offshore. Site unsuitable in northerly winds. Charge.

Banff Harbour (Moray Firth)
Harbour Slipway
Follow A 98 west of Fraserburgh, turning off at bridge between Macduff and Banff: site is in Outer Basin at root of Lighthouse Pier. Concrete slipway onto sand available for 3/4 hours either side HW and suitable all craft. Fuel, parking for car and trailer, toilets, chandlery from A Paterson, Shore St. Speed limit 3 knots in harbour. Site is very exposed in N to ENE winds: contact Harbour Master Tel Banff(02612) 5093. Charge.

Portsoy (Moray Firth)
Harbour Slipway
Follow A 98 west from Fraserburgh and signs to harbour. Concrete slipway at west end of harbour available for 3 hours either side HW and suitable all craft. Fuel, parking for car and trailer, toilets, nearest chandlers in Macduff. Speed limit 3 knots in harbour. Further information from Harbour Master Tel Banff(02612) 5093. Charge.

Cullen (Moray Firth)
Harbour Slipway
Follow A 98 west from Fraserburgh. Steep concrete slipway onto sandy beach available for 4 hours either side HW and suitable dinghies and powerboats up to 16'LOA. Fuel, parking for car and trailer, toilets. Speed limit 3mph in harbour. Further information from Mr H Runcie Tel Cullen(0542) 41116. Site is very exposed in N to W winds. No Charge.

Portknockie (Moray Firth)
Inner Basin Slipway
Turn off A 96 east of Elgin onto A 98 and onto A 942 after 12 miles: the final approach to the harbour is steep. Short concrete slipway available for 4 hours either side HW and suitable most craft. Fuel, parking for car and trailer, toilets. Speed limit 3mph in harbour. Contact Harbour Master Tel Cullen(0542) 40705. No Charge.

Findochty (Moray Firth)
Harbour Slipway
Turn off A 96 east of Elgin onto A 98 turning left into Buckie along A 942 and follow coastal road to Findochty. Long concrete slipway available for 2 hours either side HW and suitable all craft. Fuel, parking for car and trailer, toilets. Speed limit 3mph in harbour. Contact Harbour Master Tel Cullen(0542) 40705. Site is exposed in N winds. No Charge.

Buckie (Moray Firth)
Harbour Slipway
Follow A 96 east of Elgin taking A 98 and turning onto A 942 after 7 miles. Concrete slipway available for 3 hours either side HW and suitable all craft. Fuel, parking for car and trailer, crane and winch for hire, toilets, chandlers. Speed limit 3mph in harbour. Contact Harbour Master Tel Buckie(0542) 31700. No Charge.

Portgordon (Moray Firth)
Harbour Slipway
Turn off A 96 east of Elgin taking A 98 and turning onto the A 990: site is on east side of harbour. Concrete slipway available for 2/3 hours either side HW and suitable all craft. Fuel from local garage, parking for car and trailer adjacent. No Charge.

Lossiemouth (Moray Firth)
Harbour Slipway
From Elgin take A 941 for 6 miles north. Concrete slipway available at all states of tide and suitable dinghies and powerboats. Fuel, parking for car and trailer, toilets, chandlers and boatyard. Speed limit 3mph in harbour. Lossiemouth SC is nearby. Contact Harbour Master Tel Lossiemouth (034 381) 3066. No Charge but harbour dues payable.

Hopeman (Moray Firth)
Harbour Slipway
From Inverness follow A 96 east, turning onto B 9013 between Forres and Elgin and turning right onto B 9012 for 2 miles. Steep concrete slipway with winch available for 2 hours either side HW and suitable dinghies and powerboats. Fuel, parking for car and trailer, toilets, chandlers and boatyard. Speed limit 3mph in harbour. Contact Harbour Master Tel Hopeman(0343) 830650. Charge.

Burghead (Moray Firth)
Harbour Slipway
Follow A 96 east from Inverness turning onto B 9013 between Forres and Elgin. Concrete slipway onto sandy beach available at all states of tide and suitable craft up to 30'LOA. Fuel, parking for car and trailer, crane for hire, toilets, chandlers. Speed limit in harbour 3 knots. Contact Harbour Master Tel Burghead(0343) 835337. Charge.

Findhorn (Findhorn Bay, Moray Firth)
Marineland Leisure Centre
From Inverness follow A 96 east, turning off onto B 9011 at Forres and turning left at Kinloss and following road through village. Concrete slipway available at all states of tide for small craft. Fuel from Kinloss (3 miles), parking for car and trailer (c), toilets, chandlers, repairs and air compressor. No speed limit: water-skiing permitted. Findhorn Bay is a long established watersports centre. Further information Tel Findhorn(0309) 30099. Charge.

HIGHLAND

Inverness (Moray Firth)
Thornbush Slipway & Engineering Co Ltd
Follow A 9 north: site is in Anderson St at mouth of R Ness near entrance to Caledonian Canal. Concrete slipway available for 2 hours either side HW during working hours only. No fuel, parking for car and trailer (c). Speed limit: no water-skiing. Launching is affected by fast flowing river. Further information Tel Inverness(0463) 233813 Charge.

North Kessock (Moray Firth)
Old Ferry Pier
Follow A 9 north from Inverness: site is on north shore of Beauly Firth upstream of bridge. Concrete slipway available for 3 hours either side HW. Fuel, parking for car and trailer, toilets, chandlers. No Charge.

Fortrose Harbour (Moray Firth)
Chanonry SC Slipway
From A 9 north of Inverness follow A 832. Concrete slipway available for 3 hours either side HW and suitable all craft. No fuel, parking for car and trailer (c), toilets. Contact Harbour Master Tel Fortrose(0381) 20861. Charge and harbour dues payable.

Cromarty (Cromarty Firth)
The Pier
From A 9 north of Inverness take A 832. Concrete slipway available at all states of tide. Fuel, parking for car and trailer, toilets. No Charge.

Cromarty (Cromarty Firth)
Beach
From A 9 north of Inverness take A 832. Launching over shingle and firm sandy beach available at all states of tide. Fuel, parking for car and trailer, toilets. Water-skiing allowed. No Charge.

Rosskeen (Cromarty Firth)
Slipway
Follow A 9 north from Inverness and along north shore of Cromarty Firth turning off onto B 817 at Alness: site is just west of Invergordon. Concrete slipway available for 3 hours either side HW. Fuel (2/3 miles), parking for car and trailer. Water-skiing allowed with prior permission of Moray Port Authority. No Charge.

Balintore (Moray Firth)
Harbour Slipway
Follow A 9 north from Inverness, turning off south of Tain onto B 9165/6. Concrete slipway onto hard sand available at all states of tide. No fuel, parking for car and trailer, toilets, chandlers. Charge.

Hilton (Moray Firth)
The Slipway
Follow A 9 north from Inverness turning off south of Tain onto B 9165/6: site is 1 mile east of Balintore. Concrete slipway available for 3 hours either side HW. No fuel, limited parking in street, chandlers in Balintore. No Charge.

Portmahomack Harbour (Dornoch Firth)
Harbour Slipway
Turn off A 9 south of Tain onto B 9165. Stone slipway into small drying harbour available for 3 hours either side HW or launch over sandy beach at all states of tide. Petrol, parking for car and trailer, toilets. Slow speed in harbour: water-skiing allowed offshore. Contact Harbour Master for permission. Charge.

Brora Harbour (Moray Firth)
Harbour Slipway
Follow A 9 north from Inverness and minor road south of bridge to river mouth. Concrete slipway with heavy duty hand winch available for 2½ hours either side HW. Diesel on site, petrol (¼ mile), parking for car and trailer (c), no toilet, chandlers and boatyard adjacent to slipway. Charge.

Helmsdale Harbour
Turn right off A 9 north of Helmsdale river bridge into Dunrobin St, taking the next right turn down to Shore St, then turn left going to the east end of the harbour. Concrete slipway available for 4 hours either side HW and suitable all craft. Fuel, parking for car and trailer, winch, chandlers. Further information from The Harbour Master Tel Helmsdale(043 12) 347. Charge.

Lybster Harbour
Harbour Slipway
Follow A 9 south from Wick for 12 miles, turning off to village and harbour. Wooden ramp available for 2 hours either side HW. Fuel nearby, parking for car and trailer. Slow speed in harbour: water-skiing allowed offshore but site exposed in onshore winds. No Charge.

Scrabster
Thurso Bay
Follow A 882 north west from Wick: site is on west side Thurso Bay. Concrete slipway available for 3 hours either side HW and suitable all craft up to 25'LOA. Diesel, parking for car and trailer (c), toilets, crane, chandlers in Wick. Consult Harbour Master Tel Thurso(0847) 2779. Speed limit 10mph in harbour: water-skiing allowed in bay. No Charge.

Kylesku South
Ferry Slipway
From Ullapool follow A 835, A 837 and A 894 north: site is at south side of old ferry crossing. Concrete slipway available at all times. No fuel, parking for car and trailer. Charge.

Ullapool (Loch Broom)
Harbour Slipway
From Inverness follow A 832 and A 835 north. Concrete slipway available at all times except for 1 hour either side LWS. Fuel nearby, toilets. Contact Ross & Cromarty DC Tel Dingwall(0349) 6344. No Charge.

Laide (Gruinard Bay)
From Inverness follow A 862/832/835 and A 832 to the west shore of Gruinard Bay: site is $\frac{1}{2}$ mile from Post Office. Concrete and stone slipway available for 3 hours either side HW and suitable small craft. Fuel, limited parking for car and trailer. No Charge.

Aultbea (Loch Ewe)
From Inverness follow A 863, A 835 and A 832 to the east side of Loch Ewe: site is near Aultbea Hotel. Concrete and stone slipway available for 3 hours either side HW and suitable small craft only. Fuel, parking for car, leave trailer by arrangement, toilets. No Charge.

Poolewe (Loch Ewe)
From Inverness follow A 863/835 and A 832 to southern shore of Loch Ewe. Launching from concrete and stone slipway available at all states of tide except LWS. No fuel, parking for car and trailer by arrangement. No Charge.

Strath, Gairloch (Loch Gairloch)
From Inverness, follow A 862/832 and B 8021 to north shore of Loch Gairloch about 1 mile from Gairloch. Concrete and stone slipway available at all states of tide except LWS and suitable small craft. No fuel or parking. No Charge.

Gairloch (Loch Gairloch)
Pier Road
Follow A 832 from Inverness: site is on east side Loch Gairloch. Launching from tarmac surface over rock available for 3 hours either side HW for small craft or at HW for larger craft. Fuel at pier by arrangement, parking for car and trailer, toilets, chandlery and groceries from The Harbour Centre and repair and engineering facilities from J Elder. No speed limit: water-skiing allowed but do not obstruct fishing boats. Temporary membership of Club (adjacent to slipway) allows use of facilities. No Charge.

Badachro (Loch Gairloch)
From Inverness, follow A 862/832 and B 8056 to south shore of Loch Gairloch. Concrete and stone slipway available for 3 hours either side HW. No fuel, parking for car, leave trailer by arrangement. No Charge.

Stromeferry (Loch Carron)
Old Ferry Stage
Follow A 87 west from A 82, taking A 890 north: site is at old ferry site on south shore Loch Carron. Launching on either shore from concrete slipway available at all states of tide. No fuel, parking for car and trailer. Charge.

Kyle of Lochalsh
Old Ferry Slipway
Follow A 87 west from A 82. Stone slipway available for 3 hours either side HW. Fuel nearby, parking for car and trailer, toilets. Contact Harbour Master for permission to launch. Charge.

Shiel Bridge (Loch Duich)
Follow A 87 west from A 82: site is at head of loch and opposite Kintail Lodge Hotel. Stone slipway available for 2 hours either side HW. Fuel, parking for car and trailer. No Charge.

Kyleakin, Isle of Skye
Old Ferry Slipway
Site is adjacent ferry slip at Kyle of Lochalsh crossing. Concrete slipway available at all states of tide. Fuel nearby, parking for car and trailer. Do not obstruct ferry. Contact Harbour Master at Kyle of Lochalsh. Charge.

Ardvasar Bay, Isle of Skye
Sleat Marine Services
Follow A 851 from Broadford to Armadale then A 853 to Ardvasar or by ferry from Mallaig. Launch from hardstanding slope onto hard beach of sand and shingle at all states of tide and suitable craft up to 2 tons. No fuel, parking for car and trailer, limited chandlery, repair facilities. No speed limit: water-skiing allowed. Slipway may be obstructed, especially in mid March and early October. Further information Tel Ardvasar(047 14) 216. No Charge.

Stein, Waternish, Isle of Skye
From Portree, follow A 856/850 and B 986: site is on western side of Waternish Peninsula and access is via narrow roads. Narrow concrete slipway available for 4 hours either side HW. Limited fuel, limited parking for car and trailer. Water-skiing allowed except on Sundays. No Charge.

Mallaig (Sound of Sleat)
East Bay Beach
Follow A 830 west from Fort William. Narrow and fairly steep concrete slipway available for launching 1 hour either side HW. Fuel, parking for car and trailer, toilets, chandlers. No speed limit: water-skiing allowed. No Charge.

Arisaig Harbour
Arisaig Marine Ltd
Follow A 830, 33 miles west from Fort William: main road has 12½' height restriction. Concrete slipway with rails available from 0900-1800 for 4 hours either side HW and suitable vessels up to 75'LOA or launch over hard shingle at all states of tide. Diesel on site, petrol (½ mile), parking for car and trailer (c), crane and winch for hire, toilets, limited range of chandlery, repairs, moorings, shop, hotel, restaurant and accommodation. No speed limit: water-skiing allowed with permission. Further information Tel Arisaig(068 75) 224/678. Charge.

Salen (Loch Sunart)
Loch Sunart Marine Services
From Fort William follow A 830 west taking A 861 at Lochailort and B 8007 in Salen or take A 82 south from Fort William crossing Loch Linnhe on Corran Ferry and follow A 861 via Strontian to Salen: site is on north shore of Loch Sunart on the Ardnamurchan Peninsula. Launch from granite jetty 3 hours either side HW or over shingle into creek at all times. Fuel (2 miles), parking for car and trailer (c), chandlers. No speed limit: water-skiing allowed. Further information Tel Salen(096 785) 648. Charge.

Corpach (Loch Eil)
Fort William
Follow A 830 west from Fort William along north shore Loch Eil: site is ex-MTB slip owned by Wiggins Teape. Concrete slipway available at all states of tide. Fuel, parking for car and trailer, toilets, chandlery from Corpach Chandlers. Obtain permission to use before launching. Charge.

Fort William (Loch Linnhe)

Follow A 82 south west from Inverness. Concrete slipway near the pier available at all states of tide. Fuel, limited parking for car and trailer, chandlers nearby. Do not obstruct the ferries. No Charge.

Fort William (Loch Linnhe)
Lochaber YC

Follow A 82, ½ mile south from Fort William town centre: site is at junction with Ashburn Lane. Concrete slipway available for 5 hours either side HW and suitable craft up to 25'LOA. Fuel, parking for car and trailer by arrangement, crane by arrangement, toilets, repairs from Lochaber Marine, chandlery from Corpach Chandlers. Further information Tel Fort William(0397) 216. No Charge, but donation to YC appreciated.

Onich (Loch Linnhe)
Cameron Cruisers

Follow A 82 south from Fort William. Concrete slipway available for 4 hours either side HW. Fuel, parking for car and trailer (c), toilets, chandlery. Further information Tel Onich(085 53) 224. Charge.

Kentallen (Loch Linnhe)
Holly Tree Hotel

Follow A 82 and A 828 south from Fort William: site is 3 miles south of Ballachulish Bridge on east shore Loch Linnhe and adjacent pier. Concrete slipway available for 4 hours either side HW and suitable all trailed craft. No fuel, parking for car, leave trailer by arrangement with hotel. Visitors should make arrangements with hotel proprietor.

STRATHCLYDE

Bunessan, Isle of Mull
Bendoran Boatyard

Site is 1½ miles west of Bunessan off the A 849. Concrete slipway available at all states of tide. Fuel, parking for car and trailer, toilets, showers and laundry facilities, chandlery. No speed limit. Charge.

Barcaldine (Loch Creran)
Creran Moorings

From Oban follow A 828, 12 miles north: site is 1 mile north of the Sea Life Centre. Concrete slipway available during daylight hours at all states of tide except for 2 hours at LWS and suitable all craft up to 25' LOA. Fuel from Benderloch (6 miles), parking for car and trailer (c), toilets and showers, sailing school, visitors' moorings and camp site adjacent. No speed limit: water-skiing allowed. Further information Tel Ledaig(063 172) 265. Charge includes tractor assistance.

Dunstaffnage (Firth of Lorn)
Dunstaffnage Yacht Harbour

Follow A 85, 2 miles north from Oban. Launch over rock and gravel surface for 2 hours either side HW. No fuel, parking for car and trailer (c), toilets, berths, restaurant and shop. No speed limit: water-skiing allowed. Further information Tel Oban(0631) 66555. Charge

Oban (Loch Linnhe)
Ganavan Leisure Ltd

Follow A 85 north from Oban turning left to Ganavan 2 miles north of Oban: access is via a narrow road. Wide concrete slipway available at all states of tide and suitable all craft. Fuel in Oban, parking for car and trailer (c), toilets and showers, bar/restaurant, children's facilities, chandlery from Nancy Black. Charge.

Oban
Railway Pier Slipway
Follow A 85 west from Perth to Oban and signs to Car Ferries: site is at south end of town at end of railway pier. Concrete slipway available for 2 hours either side HW and suitable all craft. Fuel nearby, limited parking, toilets nearby, chandlery from Nancy Black, boatyard facilities from Oban Yacht Services. No speed limit: water-skiing allowed. Charge.

Oban
Port Beag Slip
Follow A 85 west from Perth to Oban and follow Gallanach Rd south: site is on the south side of Oban Bay, west of South Pier. Steep wide concrete slipway (1:6) available for 5 hours either side HW and suitable all craft. Fuel, parking for car and trailer ($\frac{1}{2}$ mile), chandlery from Nancy Black, repairs from D Currie. No speed limit: water-skiing allowed outside harbour. Slip may be blocked in winter by laid up boats. No Charge.

Lerags (Loch Feochan)
Ardoran Marine
Site is 5 miles south of Oban on A 816: access is via narrow road with passing places. Concrete slipway available at all states of tide. Diesel on site, parking for car and trailer (c), toilets, showers and laundry, chandlery and outboard engine repairs and spares. No water-skiing in loch but access to sea where no restrictions. Moorings and accommodation available: divers are welcome. Charge.

Balvicar, Seil
Scotport
From Oban, follow A 816 then B 844 to Seil. Two slipways, one with 1:18 gradient for craft up to 30'LOA, one with 1:20 gradient for larger craft and 12 ton crane on site; both available at all times. Fuel, parking for car and trailer, toilets, chandlery from Nancy Black, Oban. Speed limit 6 knots in harbour: water-skiing permitted offshore. Further information Tel Balvicar(085 23) 412. No Charge.

Kilmelford (Loch Melfort)
Kilmelford Yacht Haven (Camus Marine Ltd)
Follow A 816 for 16 miles south of Oban. Concrete slipway available during working hours: large boats have to be moved from trailers to slipway by hoist, smaller craft can launch from a shingle hard. Fuel, parking for car and trailer (c), toilets, chandlery. No speed limit: water-skiing allowed. Further information Tel Kilmelford(085 22) 248/279. Charge.

Kilmelford (Loch Melfort)
The Melfort Pier, The Melfort Maritime Co
Follow A 816 for 16 miles south of Oban, taking road to Degnish. Concrete slipway onto shingle beach available at all states of tide. Fuel on pier, parking for car and trailer (c), toilets, chandlery from Camus Marine. No speed limit: water-skiing allowed and full watersports facilities and accommodation available. Charge.

Loch Shuna
Craobh Haven
Follow A 816 south from Oban towards Lochgilphead: site is 20 miles south of Oban and 14 miles north of Lochgilphead. Two slipways: one concrete with travel hoist for larger craft and shingle hard at Watersport Centre for smaller craft available at all states of tide during normal working hours. Fuel, calor & camping gaz, parking for car and trailer (c), toilets & showers, chandlers, shop, pub etc. Speed limit 5mph in harbour: no water-skiing within harbour. Pontoon berths and accommodation available. Further information Tel Barbreck(085 25) 222/666. Charge.

Ardfern (Loch Craignish)
Ardfern Yacht Centre
Follow A 816 south from Oban turning onto B 8002 for 1 mile: site is at head of Loch Craignish in sheltered waters but with good access to extensive cruising grounds. Concrete slipway onto shingle available during working hours for 3 hours either side HW and suitable all craft up to 25'LOA. Fuel, parking for car and trailer (c), toilets and showers, chandlery and full marina facilities. No speed limit: water-skiing permitted. Further information Tel Barbreck(085 25) 247. Charge.

Crinan (Loch Crinan)
Crinan Ferry
Follow A 816 south from Oban, turning onto B 8025 and B 841: site is old ferry ramp at end of Crinan Canal and near the Crinan Hotel. Stone slipway available for 2/3 hours either side HW. Fuel, parking for car and trailer, toilets, chandler. Facilities for launching larger craft are available at Crinan Boats Ltd Tel Crinan(054 683) 232. No Charge.

Tayvallich (Loch Sween)
Turn off A 816 north of Lochgilphead onto B 841 and B 8025: site is on west shore of loch and access is via narrow roads. Launching from slipway available at all times. No Charge.

Ardrishaig (Loch Fyne)
Pier Square Slipway
follow A 83 south from Lochgilphead: site is adjacent main public car park and pier at east end of Crinan Canal. Fairly steep concrete slipway available for 2 hours either side HW and suitable dinghies and powerboats only. Fuel (200yds), parking for car and trailer (c), telephone, chandlers in Crinan, yard facilities from Ardrishaig Boatyard. No speed limit: water-skiing allowed in Loch Fyne. Further information Tel Lochgilphead(0546) 3210. Charge and harbour dues payable.

Tarbert (Loch Fyne)
Tarbert Yacht Club
Follow A 83 south from Lochgilphead: site is on south side of harbour in Pier Rd and adjacent clubhouse. Concrete slipway onto shingle available at all states of tide for craft up to 4 tons. Fuel nearby, parking for car and trailer (c), toilets nearby, chandlers at Crinan and repairs from McCallum Boatbuilders. Speed limit 4 knots in harbour: water-skiing permitted outside harbour. All visitors are welcome to the club, contact the Commodore, Hilary Macdonald Tel Tarbert(088 02) 219. Charge.

Campbeltown Harbour (Campbeltown Loch)
New Quay Slip, Hall Street
Follow A 83 south from Lochgilphead. Concrete slipway available for 3 hours either side HW and suitable all craft. Fuel, parking for car and trailer, toilets and showers ($\frac{1}{4}$ mile), chandlery from New Quay Chandlers, Old Quay, repairs from Campbeltown Shipyard. Speed limit in harbour: water-skiing permitted outside. Further information from the Harbour Master Tel Campbeltown(0586) 52552. No Charge but harbour dues payable.

Lamlash, Isle of Arran
Follow A 841 south from Brodick to harbour front. Concrete slipway available for 3 hours either side HW. Fuel, parking for car and trailer, toilets, chandlers. No speed limit. No Charge.

Whiting Bay, Isle of Arran
Shore Road
Follow A 841 south from Brodick: site is adjacent pier. Concrete slipway available for 2$\frac{1}{2}$ hours either side HW and suitable dinghies only. Fuel, parking for car and trailer, toilets, chandlers. No Charge.

Crarae (Loch Fyne)
Quarry Point Visitor Centre
From Glasgow follow A 82 and A 83 to west side of Loch Fyne: site is 2 miles south of Furnace. Launching over shingle available 1000-1800 April-Oct for 3 hours either side HW and suitable craft up to 20'LOA. Fuel, parking for car and trailer, toilets, restaurant, children's facilities. No speed limit: water-skiing permitted. **Note:** it is hoped to upgrade this facility soon. No Charge.

St Catherine's (Loch Fyne)
St Catherines's Slip
From Glasgow follow A 82/83 taking A 815 Dunoon Rd for 5 miles along east shore of Loch Fyne: site is opposite St Catherine's Hotel. Concrete slipway available for 4 hours either side HW and suitable all craft. Petrol, parking for car and trailer, other facilities at hotel. No speed limit: water-skiing allowed. Site is mainly used by hotel. No Charge.

Tighnabruaich (Kyles of Bute)
Kyles of Bute Boatyard
From Dunoon follow A 815/B 836/A 886 and A 8003 along west shore Kyles of Bute. Concrete slipway onto shingle available for 2 hours either side HW. Fuel from local garage, parking for car and trailer (c), toilets in village, chandlery and full boatyard facilities available. Further information Tel(070 081) 2130. Charge only if yard assistance given.

Kames, by Tighnabruaich (Kyles of Bute)
Tank Landing Slip
Leave A 83 at Cairndow taking A 815/A 886 and A 8003 south to Tighnabruaich then turn south along Shore Rd to Kames, keeping left and following signs to Ardlament. Site is 1 mile from Kames crossroads. Large concrete slipway (ex flying boat) in excellent condition available for 5 hours either side HW approx and suitable all craft up to 25'LOA. Fuel, parking for car and trailer in large car park adjacent, toilets (1 mile), chandlery and repairs from Kyles of Bute Boatyard (1½ miles). No Charge.

Colintraive (Kyles of Bute)
Ferry Stage
From Dunoon follow A 815/B 836 and A 886: launch at site of ferry crossing to Isle of Bute. Concrete slipway available for 4 hours either side HW, provided ferry is not obstructed. Fuel nearby, limited parking for car and trailer, toilets. No Charge.

Rothesay, Isle of Bute
Outer Harbour Slipway
From Argyll via Colintraive ferry and south on A 886/ 884 or from Inverclyde via Wemyss Bay ferry. Concrete slipway available for 3 hours either side HW. Fuel nearby, parking for car and trailer. No Charge.

Port Bannatyne, Isle of Bute
From Argyll via Colintraive ferry and south on A 886/884 or from Inverclyde via Wemyss Bay ferry. Concrete ramp at head of bay available at all states of tide. Fuel nearby, parking for car and trailer. No Charge.

The Port Yard, Isle of Bute
Port Bannatyne
From Argyll via Colintraive ferry and A 886/844 or from Inverclyde via Wemyss Bay ferry and A 844. Concrete slipway with rails available for 5 hours either side HW and suitable all craft. Fuel, parking for car and trailer (c), crane, winch, toilets, chandlery and repair facilities, moorings on site. No speed limit: water-skiing allowed. Further information Tel Rothesay(0700) 3171. Charge.

Dunoon (Firth of Clyde)
Port Riddell Slipway, East Bay
By ferry from Gourock. Concrete slipway available for 2 hours either side HW. Fuel nearby, limited parking for car and trailer, toilets nearby. No Charge.

Sandbank (Holy Loch)
Morris & Lorimer (Holy Loch) Ltd
By ferry from Gourock and follow A 815 north from Dunoon. Concrete slipway available for 1½ hours either side HW. No fuel, parking for car and trailer. By arrangement Tel Dunoon(0369) 214. Charge.

Clynder (Gare Loch)
Modern Charters Ltd, Victoria Place, Shore Road
Follow B 833 south from Garelochhead: access is via Shore Rd. Concrete slipway available for 2 hours either side HW. Fuel from Kilcreggan (3 miles), parking for car and trailer, toilets, chandlery and shop. Speed limit 12mph: no water-skiing. Moorings available. Further information Tel Clynder(0436) 831312. No Charge.

Rhu (Gare Loch)
Rhu Marina
From Dumbarton follow A 814 north west to eastern shore of Gare Loch. Launching by travel hoist only, available for 3 hours either side HW. Diesel, parking for car and trailer, toilets, chandlery. Speed limit 8 knots: no water-skiing. Further information Tel Rhu(0436) 820652. Charge

Helensburgh (Firth of Clyde)
Pier
Follow A 814 north west from Dumbarton and turn left at traffic lights in middle of town: site is adjacent pier. Concrete slipway available for 3 hours either side HW and suitable all craft. Fuel nearby, parking for car and trailer, toilets. Charge.

Dumbarton (Firth of Clyde)
Follow A 814 into town, turning left into the High St, right into Bridge St and right to the slipway. Concrete slipway into River Leven available for 3 hours either side HW and suitable craft up to 9'wide. Fuel, parking for car and trailer, toilets and telephone, chandlery and yard facilities from McAllisters Boatyard, Woodyard Rd. No Charge.

Renfrew (Firth of Clyde)
Clyde River Boatyard
Leave M 8 at junction 27 and follow signs to Renfrew: access is via Old King's Inch Rd. Concrete slipway available for 2½ hours either side HW and suitable all craft up to 45'LOA and 14 ton max. Diesel on site, petrol (1½ miles), parking for car and trailer (c), toilets, chandlers (3 miles), crane and hoist available. Speed limit: no water-skiing. Charge.

Erskine (River Clyde)
Erskine Ferry Quay
Leave M 8 at junction 30 and follow signs. Concrete slipway available at all states of tide. No fuel, parking for car and trailer, no toilets. Speed limit: no water-skiing. No Charge.

East Bay, Port Glasgow (River Clyde)
Coronation Park
From M 8 follow A 8 west: access is via tarred road in park. Concrete slipway available at all states of tide except LWS and suitable craft up to 25'LOA. Fuel from garage (200yds), parking for car and trailer, toilets (200yds), chandlery from Wm M Turner & Sons boatyard adjacent. No Charge.

Newark (River Clyde)
Newark Castle Park
Follow M 8 and A 8 west from Glasgow turning off at Newark roundabout. Concrete slipway available at HW only and suitable craft up to 20'LOA. Fuel, parking for car, no trailers. No Charge.

Port Glasgow (River Clyde)
Kelburn Riverside Park
Follow M 8 west turning off at Woodhall roundabout. Concrete slipway available for 2 hours either side HW and suitable craft up to 20' LOA. No fuel, parking for car and trailer, toilets (under construction). No Charge.

Greenock (River Clyde)
Battery Park
Follow A 8 to Greenock: access is from Eldon St into park. Concrete slipway onto shingle available from 0800-1630 for 2 hours either side HW and suitable craft up to 25'LOA. Fuel, parking for car and trailer, toilets, chandlery from G & R McKenzie, Gourock, repairs from Adam's BY. Permission to launch required from the Rec Services Dept, Municipal Buildings, Greenock Tel Greenock(0475) 24400 ext 378. No Charge.

Gourock (River Clyde)
Cove Road Slipway, Cardwell Bay
Follow A 8 toward Gourock turning right into Cove Road (no through road): access is narrow. Narrow concrete slipway available for 2 hours either side HW and suitable dinghies only. Fuel, no parking, chandlery from G & R McKenzie, repairs from Adams BY. No Charge.

Gourock (River Clyde)
Ashton Slipway
Follow A 8 to Gourock and signs to Ashton: site is on east side RGYC and entrance is narrow. Concrete slipway available for 2 hours either side HW and suitable dinghies only. No fuel, parking, toilets, chandlery from G & R McKenzie, repairs from Adam's BY. No Charge.

Gourock (River Clyde)
Maybank Slipway
Follow A 8 to Gourock and signs to Ashton: site has narrow entrance. Concrete slipway available for 2 hours either side HW and suitable dinghies only. No fuel, parking in main road only, toilets, chandlery from G & R McKenzie, repairs from Adam's BY. No Charge.

Inverkip (Firth of Clyde)
Kip Marina
From Greenock follow A 742 south. Launching by travel hoist only available at all states of tide. Fuel, parking for car and trailer, toilets and other facilities. Further information Tel Wemyss Bay(0475) 521485. Charge.

Largs (Firth of Clyde)
Barrfields Slipway, North Bay
Follow A 78 north from Irvine: access is via Shore Rd. Concrete slipway available for 4 hours either side HW. Fuel nearby, parking for car and trailer (100yds), toilets. Slipway is used by RNLI inshore lifeboat which must be allowed access at all times. No Charge.

Largs (Firth of Clyde)
Cairney's Quay, South Bay
Follow A 78 north from Irvine: access is via Shore Rd and car park with height restriction; no vehicular access to actual site. Concrete slipway available for 4 hours either side HW. Fuel, parking for car and trailer by arrangement with Largs SC (John St), toilets. No speed limit: water-skiing discouraged inshore. Site is mainly used by Largs SC: for visitors, Barrfields slipway is easier. No Charge.

Largs (Firth of Clyde)
Largs Yacht Haven
Follow A 78 north from Irvine: site is 1 mile south of Largs. Stone slipway available for 2 hours either side HW and suitable all craft up to 25'LOA: 50 ton travel hoist available by arrangement at all states of tide. Diesel on site, petrol (1 mile), parking for car and trailer (c), toilets and showers, chandlery, shop and other facilities. Speed limit 2 knots in marina: water-skiing permitted in Firth of Clyde. Excellent new facility: further information Tel Largs (0475) 675333. Charge for hoist only.

Great Cumbrae Is (Firth of Clyde)
Cumbrae National Water Sports Training Centre

Site is on north east corner of island. Concrete slipway available for 4 hours either side HW. Fuel from local garage, parking for car and trailer (50yds), toilets (400yds), chandlery from Largs Yacht Haven (1½ miles by sea). Use only with permission: no water-skiing. No Charge.

Great Cumbrae Is (Firth of Clyde)
Millport Harbour Slipway

Site is at south end of island. Launch from ramp in harbour for 3 hours either side HW. Fuel, parking for car and trailer. No Charge.

Saltcoats (Firth of Clyde)
Harbour Slipway

Turn off A 78 coast road. Stone ramp available for launching approx 2 hours either side HW and suitable all craft. Petrol, parking for car and trailer. No Charge.

Irvine Harbour (Firth of Clyde)
Harbour Slipway

From Glasgow follow A 737 and A 736: site is in Harbour St close to the Scottish Maritime Museum. Concrete slipway available for 3 hours either side HW. No fuel, parking for car and trailer, no toilets. By arrangement only with Irvine Watersports Club Tel Irvine(0294) 216529. No Charge.

Troon (Firth of Clyde)
Troon Marina

From Glasgow follow A 77/A 78 and A 759: access is via Harbour Rd. Concrete slipway available at all states of tide during daylight hours suitable all craft and by arrangement at weekends Tel Troon(0292) 315553. Fuel, ample parking for car and trailer, toilets and showers, chandlery from Kyle Chandlers, boat hoist and tractor available during office hours (0900-1630) and other facilities. Speed limit 3 knots in marina: water-skiing in designated area. Visitors are welcome and short term berths are available. Charge.

Ayr (Firth of Clyde)
Ayr Yacht & Cruising Club

From Glasgow follow A 77 south: site is in South Harbour St. Concrete slipway onto gravel available for 3/4 hours either side HW for larger craft or at all states of tide for dinghies. Fuel from garage (½ mile), parking for car and trailer (c), toilets, nearest chandlers at Troon. Speed limit 3 knots in harbour: water-skiing allowed in bay. Advance notice and 3rd party indemnity up to £100,000 required. Contact Hon Sec Tel Ayr(0292) 42042. Charge and harbour dues payable.

Girvan
Harbour Slipway

Turn off A 77 Bridge St onto Newton Place via The Newton Kennedy Bridge. Concrete slipway available for 4 hours either side HW and suitable all craft up to approx 30'LOA. Fuel, parking for car and trailer (c), toilets, telephone, chandlery from Girvan Chandlers, yard facilities from Noble Shipyard. Speed limit 4 knots in harbour: water-skiing permitted offshore. This is a commercial fishing harbour: do not obstruct the fleet. Charge and harbour dues payable.

DUMFRIES AND GALLOWAY

Cairnryan (Loch Ryan)
Cairnryan Slipway

Follow A 77 north from Stranraer along east shore of Loch Ryan: site is in picnic area just north of Cairnryan. Steep concrete slipway onto shingle available all states of tide suitable small craft. Fuel, parking for car and trailer, toilets. No speed limit. No Charge.

Stranraer (Loch Ryan)
Stranraer Harbour
Follow A 75 west from Dumfries: site is behind Ulster Bus Depot. Concrete slipway avalable for 2 hours either side HW. Fuel, parking for car and trailer (c), toilets. No speed limit: water-skiing allowed. No Charge.

Wig Bay (Loch Ryan)
Wig Bay Slip
Follow A 718 north from Stanraer: site is on west side of Loch Ryan south of Kirkcolm Pt. Concrete slipway available at all states of tide. Fuel, parking for car and trailer. Site is adjacent Loch Ryan SC from whom permission to launch should be obtained. No Charge.

Lady Bay (Loch Ryan)
Follow A 718 north from Stranraer: site is on west shore Loch Ryan. Concrete slipway onto sand available at all states of tide and suitable small craft only. No fuel, parking for car and trailer, picnic area. Site is private but free access is normally granted.

Portpatrick
Harbour Slipway
From Stranraer follow A 716 and A 77 west: site is on south side of Outer Harbour near disused lighthouse and access is steep and narrow and partially obstructed. Concrete slipway onto shingle and soft sand available for 2 hours either side HW and suitable dinghies only. Fuel, parking for car and trailer, toilets. Consult Harbour Master Tel Portpatrick(077 681) 286. No Charge.

Port Logan (Port Logan Bay)
From Stranraer follow A 716 south then B 7065 to Port Logan. Concrete slipway onto sand available at all states of tide and suitable small craft only. No fuel, parking for car and trailer, toilets. Water-skiing allowed. No Charge.

Mull of Galloway
From Stranraer follow A 716 south to Drummore then B 7041 and narrow track to Mull Lighthouse. Slipway of granite and stone blocks available for 2 hours either side HW. No fuel, parking for car and trailer. Site is private but free access is normally given. **Note:** there are very strong tides in the vicinity of up to 6 knots on spring tides. No Charge.

Drummore Harbour (Luce Bay)
From Stranraer follow A 716: access is directly from road at bottom of village and opposite Ship Hotel. Steep concrete slipway onto hard sand available for 2 hours either side HW and suitable dinghies. Fuel, parking for car and trailor (c), toilets. Kirkmaiden BC is nearby. No Charge.

Sandhead (Luce Bay)
Follow A 716, 8 miles south from Stranraer on west shore Luce Bay. Launching over soft sand available at any state of tide. Fuel, parking for car and trailer, toilets. Watch out for nearby bombing range signals. No Charge.

Port William (Luce Bay)
From Stranraer follow A 75 east turning onto A 747 at Glenluce: site is on east shore Luce Bay. Stone ramp onto gravel beach available 2 hours either side HW and suitable small craft only. Fuel, parking for car and trailer, toilets. No Charge.

Isle of Whithorn Harbour (Wigtown Bay)
From Stranraer follow A 75/A 747 and A 750 east. Concrete slipway available for 3 hours either side HW and suitable all craft. Fuel, parking for car and trailer, winch, toilets, chandlers. Further information from the Harbour Master Tel Whithorn(098 85) 246. Charge.

Garlieston (Wigtown Bay)

Leave the A 75 at Newton Stewart, taking A 714 south: harbour is 1 mile south of Kirkinner on B 7004, on the west side of the bay. Launching over shingle into well sheltered harbour available for 3 hours either side HW and suitable most craft. Fuel, parking for car and trailer, toilets. Contact Harbour Master, R Houston, 13 North Crescent Tel Garlieston(098 86) 259 before launching. Charge.

Brighouse Bay Holiday Park

From Kirkcudbright take A 755 west for ½ mile turning left onto B 727 signposted to Borgue: after 4 miles turn left to follow signs to Brighouse Bay and site is on right after 2 miles. Concrete slipway available at most states of tide and suitable all craft. No fuel, parking for car and trailer (c), toilets. Obtain permission to launch at site. Charge.

Kirkcudbright Harbour (Dee Estuary)
Harbour Slipway

From Dumfries follow A 75 west, turning south onto A 711: site is on east shore of estuary. Stone slipway onto shingle available for 2 hours either side HW. Fuel, parking for car and trailer, toilets, chandlers. Speed limit: water-skiing allowed offshore. Further information from the Harbour Master Tel Kirkcudbright(0557) 31135. No Charge but harbour dues payable.

Kirkcudbright (Dee Estuary)
Gibb Hill Sawmill

From Dumfries follow A 75 west, turning south onto A 711 and crossing to west shore of estuary and adjacent Gibb Hill Sawmill. Concrete slipway available for 3/4 hours either side HW. Fuel nearby, limited parking for car and trailer. Charge.

Kippford

Follow A 711 from Dumfries to Dalbeattie and A 710 4 miles south. Concrete slipway onto shingle available for 2 hours either side HW. Fuel, parking for car and trailer, toilets, chandler. No Charge.

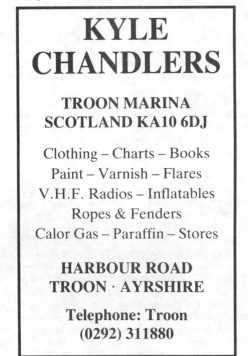

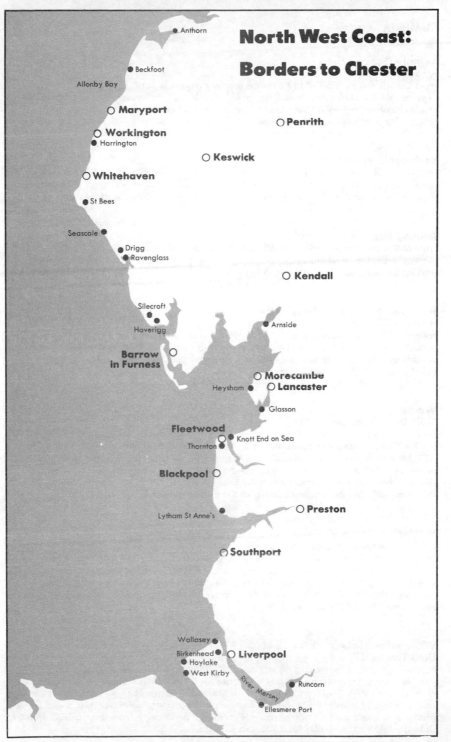

North West Coast: Borders to Chester

- Anthorn
- Beckfoot
- Allonby Bay
- ○ Maryport
- ○ Workington
  - Harrington
- ○ Penrith
- ○ Keswick
- ○ Whitehaven
- St Bees
- Seascale
- Drigg
- Ravenglass
- ○ Kendall
- Silecroft
- Haverigg
- Arnside
- Barrow in Furness ○
- ○ Morecambe
- Heysham ○ Lancaster
- Glasson
- Fleetwood ○ Knott End on Sea
- Thornton
- Blackpool ○
- Lytham St Anne's
- ○ Preston
- ○ Southport
- Wallasey
- Birkenhead ○ Liverpool
- Hoylake
- West Kirby
- River Mersey
- Runcorn
- Ellesmere Port

CUMBRIA

Anthorn (Solway Firth)
Foreshore
From Carlisle follow B 5307 to Kirkbride then minor roads north for 4 miles. Launching over shingle foreshore available 2 hours either side HW and suitable light craft which can be manhandled only. Fuel from local garage, parking for car and trailer. Site suitable for dinghies only. No Charge.

Beckfoot (Solway Firth)
Follow B 5300, 4 miles south of Silloth, where the road runs alongside the beach. Launching over shingle beach available near HW and suitable small craft only. No fuel, parking for car and trailer. Water-skiing permitted but site is exposed. No Charge.

Allonby Bay (Solway Firth)
From Maryport take A 596 and B 5300, 5 miles north to Allonby village. Concrete slipway available at all states of tide and suitable dinghies and powerboats. No fuel, parking for car and trailer. Water-skiing permitted but site is exposed. No Charge.

Maryport Harbour (Solway Firth)
Harbour Slipway
Follow A 596 south from Carlisle: site is behind coastguard station. Concrete slipway available 2½ hours either side HW. Fuel, parking for car and trailer (c), toilets. Speed limit in harbour: water-skiing allowed offshore. Apply to the Dockmaster, Maryport Harbour Tel Maryport(0900) 817440. Charge.

Workington
Tidal Dock (Vanguard SC)
Follow A 596 south from Carlisle: site is on south side of dock just seaward of the railway bridge. Concrete slipway available for 2½ hours either side HW for trailed craft up to 35'LOA: smaller craft can be launched 4/5 hours either side HW. Fuel in town (1 mile), parking for car and trailer. Slow speed in harbour: water-skiing allowed to seaward of Lifeboat mooring. Further information Tel Brampton(069 77) 2949. Visitors are welcome to use the slipway: assoc. membership of the club is available. Charge.

Harrington Harbour
Harbour Slipway (Harrington S & FC)
Follow B 5296 3 miles south of Workington. Concrete slipway available for 2 hours either side HW. Fuel, parking for car and trailer, toilets. This is a small port giving access to exposed open sea conditions which is not suitable for dinghies and inflatables: site recommended only for trailer-sailers. For further information and permission to launch Tel Harrington(0946) 830600. No Charge.

Whitehaven (Solway Firth)
Lime Tongue Slipway
Follow A 595 north branching off at Looe Rd: site is between Lime Tongue and Sugar Tongue Quays. Steep stone slipway available for 2 hours either side HW and suitable all craft up to 18'LOA. Fuel from Donnans Fish Merchant, Sugar Tongue; parking for car and trailer, toilets in Market Place. Speed limit 5mph in harbour: water-skiing allowed offshore. This is a busy fishing harbour. Permission and advice from the Harbour Master, Duke St, Tel Whitehaven(0946) 2435. No Charge.

St Bees
Beach
Follow A 595 and B 5345 south of Workington and local roads to beach. Concrete slipway available for 2 hours either side HW and suitable small craft only. No fuel, parking for car and trailer, no toilets. Site very exposed in onshore winds. No Charge.

Seascale
Beach
Follow A 595 south from Whitehaven turning off onto B 5344 at Gosforth. Launching over shingle beach available to light craft in offshore winds only. No fuel, parking for car and trailer. No Charge.

Drigg
Beach
Follow A 595 south from Whitehaven turning off onto B 5344 and following minor roads over railway line and to shore (1 mile). Launching over pebble and sand beach available at HW and suitable light craft only. Site is dangerous in onshore winds. No Charge.

Ravenglass
Turn off A 595 into village on shore of natural harbour formed by the rivers Irt, Mite and Esk. Ramp at end of village street can be used for launching 2 hours either side HW or launch from beaches in harbour. Fuel from garage, parking for car and trailer nearby. Harbour entrance can be dangerous in onshore winds and currents within the harbour are very strong. No Charge.

Silecroft
Beach
Follow A 595 south from Whitehaven, following the minor road which leads off at the junction of A 595 and A 5093. Launching for small craft over sand and pebble beach available near HW. Site dangerous in onshore winds. No Charge.

Haverigg
Follow A 595 and A 5093 south to Millom taking minor roads to Haverigg: site is at mouth of Duddon Estuary and close Rugby Union Club. Concrete slipway available for 2½ hours either side HW. No fuel, parking for car and trailer. No Charge.

Barrow-in-Furness
Earnsie Bay, Isle of Walney
From A 590 cross Jubilee Bridge, turning right onto the promenade and follow signs to Park Vale Sports Ground: turn right opposite Sports Ground and follow road to end. Concrete slipway available for 3 hours either side HW and suitable small craft only. Fuel in town, parking for car and trailer (c), toilets. Site is exposed in onshore winds. No Charge.

Arnside
Promenade
Leave M 6 at junction 36 taking B 6385 and B 5282: site is adjacent Crossfields Boatyard at seaward end of promenade. Concrete slipway onto soft mud available at all states of tide. Fuel, parking for car and trailer (c), toilets in village. Visitors are welcome at the Arnside SC on promontory at end of Promenade. Beware of strong tides and the "bore" in the Kent estuary. No Charge.

LANCASHIRE

Morecambe (Morecambe Bay)
Promenade
Turn off M 6 at junction 34 taking A 683 and A 589 to the seafront: site is opposite Town Hall and adjacent Morecambe and Heysham YC. Concrete slipway available 2 hours either side HW and suitable small craft only. Fuel nearby, parking for car and trailer (c), toilets, chandlery from E Nicholson, 164 Lancaster Rd. Speed limit 5mph inshore: water-skiing allowed offshore. Wooden slipway adjacent is used by YC for dinghy racing. No parking on slipway or promenade. No Charge.

Glasson Dock (River Lune)
Glasson Basin Yacht Harbour
Turn off M 6 at junction 34 taking A 588 and B 5290: site is on south bank R Lune. Concrete slipway into locked canal basin: gates to outer harbour open one hour before HW. Fuel, parking for car and trailer (c), toilets and showers, chandlery, crane, winch and boatyard facilities. Speed limit 4 knots. By arrangement only Tel Galgate(0524) 751491. Charge and harbour dues payable.

Glasson Dock
Glasson SC, Fishnet Place
From M 6/A 6 at Lancaster take A 588 south turning off onto B 5290 at Conder Green: access to site is restricted. Concrete slipway available for 2 hours either side HW and suitable dinghies and trailer-sailers up to 20'LOA. Fuel, parking for car, leave trailer by arrangement with club only, winch, chandlery and boatyard facilities adjacent (Glasson Basin Yacht Co). By arrangement with club only: contact Hon Sec Tel Lancaster(0524) 37883. Charge and harbour dues payable.

Knott-End-on-Sea (River Wyre)
Knott End Ferry Stage
Turn off A 588 from Lancaster onto B 5270: site is at ferry terminal opposite Fleetwood. Concrete slipway available at all states of tide but best for 2 hours either side HW. No fuel, parking for car and trailer, no toilets. Do not obstruct the ferries. Charge.

Thornton (River Wyre)
Stanah Car Park
From M 55 follow A 585 towards Fleetwood, turning right into Skipool Rd, then right into River Rd. Concrete slipway (1:10) available 2 hours either side HW and suitable craft up to 25'LOA. No fuel, parking for car and trailer, toilets. No Charge.

Blackpool
Little Bispham
Leave M 55 and follow signs to seafront: site is to the north of the town centre. Concrete ramp onto a sand and shingle beach available at all states of tide for launching dinghies. No fuel, parking for car and trailer (c), toilets. Speed limit 8 knots within 200m LWS mark: water-skiing in designated area. No Charge.

Blackpool
Starr Gate
Leave M 55 and follow signs to seafront: site is to south of town centre. Concrete ramp onto sand and shingle beach available at all states of tide and suitable all craft. Fuel, parking for car and trailer (c), toilets. Speed limit 8 knots within 200m LWS mark: water-skiing in designated area. No Charge.

Lytham St Anne's (Ribble Estuary)
Central Beach Slipway
Leave M 55 at junction 4 taking minor roads south and following signs to seafront.
Concrete slipway available for 2/3 hours either side HW. Fuel nearby, parking for car
and trailer (c), toilets, chandlery and repairs from Lytham Marine, Dock Rd. No Charge.

Lytham St Anne's (Ribble Estuary)
Lytham Marine Ltd, Dock Road
Leave M 55 at junction 4 following minor roads: access is via Dock Rd. Concrete slipway
available for 2 hours either side HW. Fuel, parking for car and trailer (c), toilets and
showers, chandlery. Speed limit: water-skiing permitted in river. All boatyard facilities
available 7 days a week. For further information Tel Lytham(0253) 735531. Charge.

Preston (River Ribble)
Preston Marina, Riversway Estate
Follow A 583: access is via Peddars Lane. Launching by hoist only into 400 acre locked
basin with gates opening into tidal river 1½ hours either side HW and suitable all craft.
Diesel, parking for car and trailer (c), toilets and showers, chandlery. Speed limit 4 knots.
This is a new facility which is still being developed. For further information Tel(0772)
733595. Charge.

MERSEYSIDE

Liverpool Marina (Mersey Estuary)
Coburg Dock
Follow signs to Albert Dock complex from Inner King Road: marina is in restored Coburg
Dock. Large concrete slipway into locked basin available during normal working hours:
site gives access to dock complex or to tidal river through lock gates in Brunswick Dock
which open approx 2½ hours either side HW (25th Mar-31st Oct) or by arrangement.
Fuel, parking for car and trailer, toilets, and all marina facilities on site. For further
information Tel 061-872-8041. Charge and licence required.
Further details of launching facilities in the Albert Dock complex are given on page 122.

Wallasey (Mersey Estuary)
New Brighton
Follow M 53 to Wallasey and signs to seafront: site is near pier. Concrete slipway onto
hard sand available at all states of tide. Fuel, parking for car and trailer. No speed limit:
water-skiing allowed. The Mersey is a busy commercial river and the currents are strong
here: seek local advice before launching. No Charge.

Hoylake
Promenade
Follow M 53 to Wallasey then A 551/A 553. Concrete slipways onto sand available for 2
hours either side HW. Fuel, parking for car and trailer. No speed limit: water-skiing
allowed. Exposed site in onshore winds. No Charge.

West Kirby
Promenade
Leave M 53 at junction 2 following A 551/A 553 to seafront: site is at south end of
Promenade. Concrete slipway available for 2 hours either side HW. Fuel nearby, limited
parking for car and trailer, toilets nearby. No Charge.

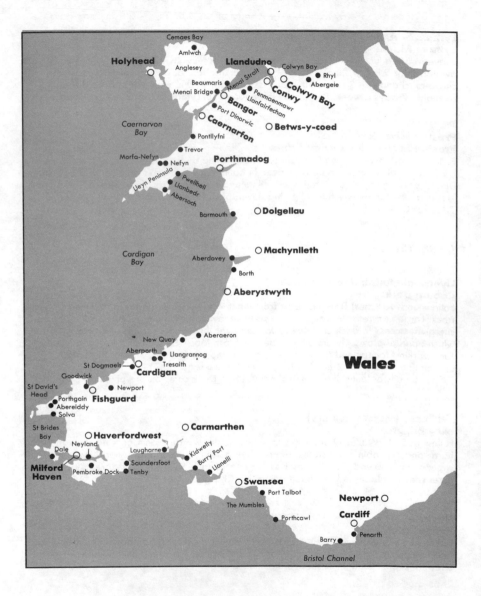

Cemaes Bay
Amlwch
Holyhead
Anglesey
Llandudno
Colwyn Bay
Rhyl
Beaumaris
Menai Strait
Colwyn Bay
Abergeie
Menai Bridge
Bangor
Penmaenmawr
Conwy
Llanfairfechan
Port Dinorwic
Caernarvon
Bay
Caernarfon
Betws-y-coed
Pontllyfni
Trevor
Morfa-Nefyn
Nefyn
Porthmadog
Lleyn Peninsula
Pwellheli
Llanbedr
Abersoch
Barmouth
Dolgellau
Cardigan
Bay
Machynlleth
Aberdovey
Borth
Aberystwyth
New Quay
Aberaeron
Aberporth
Wales
St Dogmaels
Llangrannog
Tresaith
Goodwick
Cardigan
St David's
Head
Newport
Porthgain
Fishguard
Abereiddy
Solva
St Brides
Bay
Haverfordwest
Carmarthen
Dale
Neyland
Laugharne
Kidwelly
Burry Port
Milford
Haven
Pembroke Dock
Saundersfoot
Tenby
Llanelli
Swansea
Port Talbot
Newport
The Mumbles
Cardiff
Porthcawl
Barry
Penarth
Bristol Channel

100

CLWYD

Rhyl
Rhyl Yacht Club, Foryd Harbour
Follow A 55 from Chester, turning off onto A 525 and A 548: site is on south side of bridge. Concrete slipway available for 2 hours either side HW. Fuel from local garage, parking for car and trailer (c), toilets in clubhouse. Speed limit 5mph: water-skiing permitted outside harbour. By prior arrangement only. Charge.

Kinmel Bay
Seafront
Follow A 55 from Chester, turning off onto A 548: access is via St Asaph Ave and across pedestrian promenade. Short concrete ramp onto soft sandy beach available at all states of tide for small craft which can be manhandled. Fuel (250yds), parking for car and trailer, toilets (200yds), chandlers nearby. Speed limit within 200m shore: water-skiing permitted outside limit. Site faces NW and is exposed. No Charge.

Abergele
Pensarn Beach
Follow A 55 from Chester to seafront at Pensarn. Launching across shingle bank onto sand available near HW and suitable small craft which can be manhandled. Fuel (250yds), parking for car and trailer, toilets (100yds). Speed limit within 200m shore: access lane for water-skiing provided. Site is difficult and exposed. No Charge.

Llanddulas (Colwyn Bay)
Llanddulas Beach
Follow A 55 west from Chester. Launching from short concrete ramp through coast protection works onto shingle and sand available at all states of tide and suitable craft which can be manhandled. Fuel, parking for car and trailer, toilets. Speed limit within 200m shore: water-skiing permitted offshore. Site faces north and is difficult and exposed. No Charge.

Old Colwyn (Colwyn Bay)
Old Colwyn Slipway
Follow A 55 from Chester: access is via promenade. Short concrete ramp onto shingle and sand available near HW and suitable small craft which can be manhandled. Fuel (1 mile), parking for car and trailer on promenade (50yds), toilets nearby. Speed limit within 200m shore: water-skiing permitted outside limit. Site difficult and exposed and level of beach is liable to change. No Charge.

Colwyn Bay
Dingle Slipway
Follow A 55 from Chester: access is across pedestrian promenade. Steep concrete ramp onto sand available near HW suitable small craft which can be manhandled. Fuel (1 mile), parking for car and trailer on promenade, toilets (20yds). Speed limit within 200m sea wall: water-skiing permitted outside limit but there is no provision for skiing from the shore. Site is very close to groyne, and exposed. No Charge.

Rhos-on-Sea
Aberhod Slipway
Follow A 55 from Chester turning onto A 546 and minor roads: access is via promenade. Concrete slipway onto sand available at all states of tide but best for 4 hours either side HW suitable small craft which can be manhandled. Fuel (200yds), parking for car and trailer on promenade, toilets (100yds). Speed limit within 200m shore: access lane for water-skiing provided. Site is sheltered and used by local SC. No Charge.

GWYNEDD

Deganwy (River Conwy)
Follow A 55 north east from Bangor, taking A 546 north: site is on east side of estuary at rear of station. Concrete slipway available at all states of tide. Fuel, parking for car and trailer, chandlers. Launch only with Harbour Master's permission Tel Conwy(0492) 596253. No Charge.

Conwy (Conway Bay)
Conwy Morfa
Follow A 55 west from Conwy turning right at the Fire Station, $\frac{1}{2}$ mile out of town. Steep concrete slipway available for 3 hours either side HW suitable craft up to 14'LOA (max weight 500lbs): no Jet Skies or windsurfers. Fuel, parking for car and trailer (c). Speed limit 5 mph inshore: vessels must have 3rd party insurance to £25000 and silencer. Further information from the Harbour Master Tel Conwy(0492) 596253. Charge. **Note:** due to increasing activity of Conwy immersed tube tunnel project, vessels must only navigate within marked channels in harbour at slow speed and keep clear of working areas, dredgers and barges.

Penmaenmawr (Conway Bay)
New Promenade
Take A 55 expressway to Penmaenmawr: access is via road over expressway at Western end of Promenade. Concrete slipway onto hard sand available for 3 hours either side HW or at all times for craft which can be manhandled and suitable all craft up to 25'LOA. Fuel, parking for car and trailer, toilets, telephone, nearest chandlers in Conwy (6 miles). Speed limit 10mph within 200m of the water's edge. Penmaenmawr YC is adjacent and offers temporary membership to visitors. Further information from the Harbour Master Tel Penmaenmawr(0492) 596253. No Charge.

Llanfairfechan (Conway Bay)
Llanfairfechan Sailing Club, The Promenade
Follow A 55 west from Conwy. Concrete slipway available at all states of tide. No fuel, parking for car and trailer (c), toilets in clubhouse, dinghy park, temporary membership available to visitors. Further information Tel Llanfairfechan(0248) 680301. Charge.

Menai Strait: tidal streams run strongly in the narrow channel between Anglesey and the mainland coast and this is especially so in the "Swellies", the stretch between the bridges where passage should only be attempted at HW slack.

Bangor (Menai Strait)
A M Dickie & Sons, Garth Road
From town centre follow signs to Garth. Concrete slipway available for 1$\frac{1}{2}$ hours either side HW. Fuel, parking for car and trailer (c), chandlery. By prior arrangement only Tel Bangor(0248) 352775. Charge.

ANGLESEY

Menai Bridge (Menai Strait)
Seafront
Follow A 5 over bridge, turning into Beach Rd then Water Rd. Broad concrete slipway available at all states of tide. Fuel nearby, limited parking for car and trailer. Tides run very fast here and local advice should be taken before launching. No Charge.

Beaumaris
Anglesey Boat Co Ltd, Gallows Point
Follow A 545 east from Menai Bridge: site is $\frac{1}{2}$ mile outside Beaumaris. Concrete slipway available from 0900-1800(1700 in winter) or at other times by arrangement for 3$\frac{1}{2}$ hours either side HW and suitable all craft. Fuel, parking for car and trailer (c), tractor available, toilets nearby, chandlery. Speed limit 8 knots inshore. Further information Tel Beaumaris(0248) 810359. Charge.

Benllech
Seafront
Follow A 5025 about 10 miles north from Menai Bridge and signs to Benllech Sands. Concrete slipway onto sandy beach available at all states of tide suitable small craft which can be manhandled. Fuel nearby, parking for car and trailer. Speed limit 8 knots: water-skiing permitted outside restricted area. Site is suitable in settled conditions only. No Charge.

Amlwch
Inner Harbour Slipway
Follow A 5025 north from Menai Bridge: site is on north coast. Concrete slipway available for 1½ hours either side HW. Fuel, parking for car and trailer (200yds), toilets; Amlwch Port Boat Club is open to non-members. Dead slow speed in harbour: no water-skiing. This is a fishing and commercial harbour: while visiting yachts are welcome it is advisable to contact the Dockmaster first, Tel Amlwch(0407) 831 049. No Charge.

Cemaes Bay
Harbour Slipway
Follow A 5025 north from Menai Bridge: site is on north coast of Anglesey. Wide concrete slipway into small drying harbour available for 2 hours either side HW suitable all craft. Fuel, parking for car and trailer. Speed limit 8 knots inshore. Access can be very congested. No Charge.

Holyhead
Newry Beach
Follow A 5 onto Holy Is: site is 100yds past Coastguard Station. Concrete slipway available for 3 hours either side HW. Fuel, parking for car and trailer, chandlery from Holyhead Chandlery. Speed limit in harbour: water-skiing permitted offshore. Further information from the Harbour Master Tel Holyhead(0407) 2304. Charge.

Llanfairpwll (Menai Strait)
Plas Coch Hotel & Caravan Park
Follow A 5 over Menai Bridge, turning left onto A 4080. Concrete slipway available at all states of tide. No fuel, parking for car and trailer, toilets and showers. By prior arrangement only Tel Llanfairpwll (0248) 714272/714295. Charge.

GWYNEDD

Port Dinorwic(Menai Strait)
Port Dinorwic Yacht Harbour
Turn off A 487, 3 miles west of Bangor. Two concrete slipways available for 3½/4 hours either side HW suitable all craft. Diesel, parking for car and trailer (c), toilets and showers, chandlery, berths. There are strong tidal currents here. Further information Tel Port Dinorwic(0248) 670559/671010. Charge and harbour dues payable.

Plas Menai (Menai Strait)
Plas Menai National Watersports Centre
Leave Bangor on A 487: site is 1 mile after Port Dinorwic. Concrete slipway with winch available 4 hours either side HW. Fuel from garage, parking for car and trailer (c), toilets, chandlery from A M Dickie, Bangor. No speed limit: water-skiing permitted. Prior notice is necessary Tel Port Dinorwic(0248) 670964: times are restricted by Centre use and launching is at owner's risk. Charge.

Pontllyfni (Caernarvon Bay)
Turn off A 499 Pwllheli to Caernarfon road: site is adjacent West Point Beach Holiday Camp. Concrete slipway onto shingle and sand available at all states of tide suitable craft up to 15'LOA. Fuel, parking for car and trailer. No speed limit: water-skiing allowed. No Charge.

Trevor (Lleyn Peninsula)
Harbour Slipway
Turn off A 499 Pwllheli to Caernarfon Road. Concrete slipway available for 3 hours either side HW. No fuel, parking for car and trailer. Speed limit 8 knots inshore. No Charge.

Nefyn (Lleyn Peninsula)
Beach
From Caernarfon follow A 487/499 and B 4417: site is on north shore of peninsula. Launching over hard shingle beach available at all states of tide except LWS. No fuel, parking for car and trailer (not on beach). Speed limit 8 knots inshore: water-skiing permitted in designated areas. No Charge.

Morfa-Nefyn (Lleyn Peninsula)
Beach
From Caernarfon follow A 487/499 and B 4417: site is on north shore of peninsula. Launching over hard shingle beach in Porth Dinllaen, a sheltered north-facing bay, available at all states of tide except LWS and suitable small craft only. No fuel, parking for car and trailer (not on beach). Speed limit 8 knots inshore: water-skiing permitted in designated area offshore. No Charge.

Abersoch (Cardigan Bay)
Abersoch Boatyard, The Saltings
From Porthmadog follow A 497 and A 499 west. Launching by tractor over shingle and sand beach available at all states of tide. Fuel, parking for car and trailer, toilets, chandlery. Speed limit 8 knots inshore: water-skiing allowed offshore with access lane to the shore. By prior arrangement Tel Abersoch(075 881) 2213. Charge.

Abersoch (Cardigan Bay)
Porth Fawr
From Porthmadog follow A 497 and A 499 west. Concrete slipway available at all states of tide. Fuel ($\frac{1}{2}$ mile), parking for car and trailer (c), toilets in car park, chandlery from Abersoch Boatyard. Speed limit 8 knots inshore: water-skiing permitted outside restricted area. Charge.

Abersoch (Cardigan Bay)
Golf Road Beach Entrance
From Porthmadog follow A 497 and A 499 to Abersoch village, turning first left into Golf Rd: access to site is through car park. Concrete slipway onto firm sand available from 0600-2200 at all states of tide and suitable craft up to 20'LOA. Fuel, parking for car and trailer, chandlery from Abersoch Boatyard. Charge (pay car park attendant).

Pwllheli (Cardigan Bay)
Outer Harbour
Follow A 497 west from Porthmadog: site is adjacent Firmhelm Ltd. Concrete slipway available for 3 hours either side HW suitable craft up to 20'LOA. Fuel nearby, parking for car and trailer (c), toilets, chandlery from Firmhelm. Speed limit 6 knots in harbour area: water-skiing permitted outside restricted area. All facilities including travel lift and crane available at boatyard. Further information from the Harbour Master Tel Pwllheli(0758) 613131 ext 281. Charge.

Pwllheli (Cardigan Bay)
Outer Harbour (Wm Partington Marine Ltd)
Follow A 497 west from Porthmadog. Concrete slipway available for 2/3 hours either side HW suitable all craft. Fuel nearby, parking for car and trailer (c), toilets, chandlery, crane and winch available from yard staff. Speed limit 6 knots in harbour area: water-skiing permitted outside restricted area. Further information Tel Pwllheli(0758) 612808. Charge.

Pwllheli (Cardigan Bay)
Promenade
Follow A 497 west from Porthmadog. Concrete ramps onto sandy beach available at all states of tide suitable craft which can be manhandled. Fuel nearby, parking for car and trailer, toilets and chandlers nearby. Speed limit 8 knots inshore. No Charge.

Black Rock Sands (Tremadog Bay)
Porthmadog
Follow Morfa Bychan road west from town and signs to beach. Launching over firm beach available at all states of tide and suitable small craft. No fuel, parking for car and trailer on beach. Speed limit 8 knots inshore. No Charge.

Porthmadog (Glaslyn Estuary)
Harbour Slipway
Follow A 470 south from Conwy, turning onto A 487: after crossing Britannia Bridge at N end of toll road, take first left, turning left again at T junction into Lombard St and site is ahead. Concrete slipway available at all states of tide and suitable all craft. Fuel, parking for car (c), leave trailer by arrangement with Harbour Master, chandlery from Glaslyn Marine, several boatyards nearby. Speed limit 6 knots to east 4° 09' : water-skiing allowed outside buoyed areas. Users of the site are requested to keep the access to the site clear and to observe the bye-laws, especially those which apply to powercraft. Further information from the Harbour Master Tel Porthmadog(0766) 2927. Charge.

Porthmadog (Glaslyn Estuary)
Porthmadog and Trawsfynydd SC, The Tilewhart
From Pen y Cei on west side of harbour follow narrow road right to the end. Steep concrete slipway with electric winch available for 3 hours either side HW during daylight hours only and suitable dinghies up to 17' LOA (no catamarans allowed). Fuel, parking for car and trailer, crane by arrangement, toilets, chandlery from Glaslyn Marine. Speed limit in harbour. Temporary membership of club necessary. Charge.

Llanbedr, Shell Island
Leave A 496 south of Harlech and follow minor road by church in Llanbedr 2 miles west, across causeway (not passable within 1 hour HW) to privately owned island. Concrete slipway available for 3 hours either side HW and suitable small craft only. No fuel, parking for car and trailer, toilets and other facilities on camp site. Obtain permission to launch from owners at site: daily visitors are welcome. Charge.

Barmouth Harbour (Mawddach Estuary)
Harbour Slipway
Turn off A 470 from Conwy at Dolgellau onto A 496 turning left under railway bridge: site is at mouth of the Mawddach estuary. Concrete slipway onto soft sand available 2 hours either side HW suitable all craft. Fuel, parking for car and trailer (c), crane by arrangement, toilets, chandlers. Speed limit 5 knots: water-skiing allowed outside limits with Harbour Master's permission only. Contact Harbour Master Tel Barmouth(0341) 280671 before launching. Charge and harbour dues payable.

Aberdovey (Dovey Estuary)
Dovey Inn Slipway
Turn off A 487 from Cardigan onto A 493 at Machynlleth. Concrete slipway onto hard packed shingle and mud available at all states of tide except for 1 hour either side LWS and suitable all craft. Fuel ($\frac{1}{2}$ mile), parking for car (c), (trailers can be left on beach), toilets (50yds), crane by arrangement, chandlery from Dovey Marine, The Square. Speed limit 5 knots within moorings. Site can be congested: evidence of 3rd party insurance must be shown. Further information from the Harbour Master Tel Aberdovey(065 472) 626. Charge and harbour dues payable

Aberdovey (Dovey Estuary)
Dovey Yacht Club
Turn off A 487 north of Machynlleth onto A 493 to Aberdovey. Concrete slipway onto sand available at all states of tide and suitable dinghies only. Fuel, parking for car and trailer (¼ mile) (c), crane, toilets, chandlery from Dovey Marine, repairs from West Wales Marine. Speed limit 5 knots in moorings: no powercraft allowed. Temporary membership of club required: contact The Secretary, 5 Muchall Rd, Penn, Wolverhampton. Charge.

DYFED

Ynyslas, Borth (Dovey Estuary)
Aber Leri Boatyard
Follow A 487 and B 4572 north from Aberystwyth: site is on south shore of Dovey estuary and access is via F L Steelcraft's Yard. Concrete slipway available for 2½/3 hours either side HW. No fuel, parking for car and trailer, toilets. Speed limit 4 knots in moorings: water-skiing allowed outside limits. Site most suitable for sailing craft. Charge.

Borth (Cardigan Bay)
Slipway
From the north leave A 487, taking B 4353 or from Aberystwyth take A 487 and B 4572 north. Concrete slipway available for 3 hours either side HW and suitable dinghies and trailer-sailers. Fuel, parking for car and trailer, toilets, chandlers in Aberystwyth. Speed limit 8 knots inshore. No Charge.

Aberystwyth (Cardigan Bay)
Harbour Slipway
Follow A 487 north from Cardigan to main promenade in town and follow signs south to harbour. Two concrete slipways available for 3 hours either side HW suitable craft up to 20'LOA. Fuel, parking for car and trailer, toilets, chandlers. Speed limit 5 knots within harbour limits: water-skiing permitted offshore. Contact Harbour Master at office on inner end of Town Quay Tel Aberystwyth(0970) 611433. Charge.

Aberaeron (Cardigan Bay)
South Beach
Follow A 487, 16 miles south from Aberystwyth. Conrete slipway available for 2½ hours either side HW for larger boats or at all times for dinghies. Fuel, parking for car and trailer (c), toilets. Speed limit 8 knots. Contact Harbour Master Tel Aberaeron(0545) 570407. Charge.

New Quay (Cardigan Bay)
Harbour Slipway
Turn off A 487 north of Cardigan at Synod Inn or at Llanarth onto A 486. Access is via a steep one-way street. Concrete slipway available near HW and suitable all craft. Fuel, limited parking, toilets nearby. Speed limit 8 knots inshore: water-skiing permitted outside restricted area. Contact Harbour Master before launching Tel New Quay(0545) 560368. Charge.

Llangrannog (Cardigan Bay)
Slipway
Follow A 487 north from Cardigan, turning off onto B 4334. Access to site is via narrow roads. Concrete slipway available for 3 hours either side HW and suitable dinghies and trailer-sailers. Petrol, parking for car and trailer (c). Speed limit 8 knots inshore. No Charge.

Tresaith (Cardigan Bay)
Beach
Follow A 487 north from Cardigan, turning off onto minor roads at Tan-y-groes: access to site is via narrow road. Launching over shingle beach available at all states of tide for small craft. No fuel, parking for car and trailer (c), toilets. Speed limit 8 knots inshore. No Charge.

Aberporth (Cardigan Bay)
Slipway
Follow A 487 north from Cardigan turning off at Blaenannerch onto B 4333: access is via a narrow approach road. Steep concrete slipway available for launching 3 hours either side HW and suitable dinghies and trailer-sailers. Petrol, parking for car and trailer (c), toilets. Speed limit 8 knots inshore. No Charge.

Cardigan (River Teifi)
St Dogmaels
Follow B 4546, 2 miles west from town centre: site is on west bank of Teifi Estuary. Concrete slipway available for 1½ hours either side HW and suitable craft up to 20'LOA. Fuel, parking and toilets in village, chandlers in Cardigan. Speed limit in estuary: water-skiing allowed in designated areas only. At low water there is very little water in the estuary: beware strong currents. No Charge.

Newport (Newport Bay)
Newport Sands
Follow 487 east from Fishguard: site is 2 miles beyond Newport town. Launching over hard sandy beach available at all states of tide suitable small craft only. No fuel, parking for car and trailer (c), toilets. Speed limit 8 knots inshore. No Charge.

Newport (Newport Bay)
Parrog
Follow A 487 east from Fishguard turning off in Newport: access is through car park. Concrete slipway onto hard sand available for 3 hours either side HW. Fuel in town, parking for car and trailer, toilets. Speed limit 8 knots in estuary: no water-skiing. Site ideal for dinghies and windsurfers but awkward for larger craft: beware strong currents. No Charge.

Dinas Head (Newport Bay)
Cwym Yr Eglwys
Turn off A 487 east of Fishguard at Dinas Cross: site is on east side Dinas Head and access has sharp 90° bend. Small concrete slipway onto sandy beach available at all states of tide for small boats. No fuel, parking for car and trailer (c), toilets. Speed limit 8 knots inshore. No Charge.

Dinas Head (Fishguard Bay)
Pwllgwaelod
Turn off A 487 east of Fishguard: site is on west side Dinas Head. Concrete slipway onto hard sand available at all states of tide for small craft. No fuel, parking for car and trailer, toilets, café. Speed limit 8 knots inshore. No Charge.

Fishguard (Fishguard Bay)
Lower Town
Follow A 487 from Cardigan: site is at end of quay. Concrete slipway onto hard sand available at all states of tide suitable dinghies. No fuel, parking for car and trailer, toilets. Speed limit 6 knots in harbour: no water-skiing. Access is very narrow: large boats should use Goodwick slipway. Contact Harbour Master Tel Fishguard(0348) 873320. No Charge.

Fishguard (Fishguard Bay)
Goodwick Slipway (Ferry Port)
Follow A 487 from Cardigan: site is adjacent to car park on seafront. Concrete slipway available for 2 hours either side HW suitable all craft. Fuel, parking for car and trailer, toilets, chandlery. Speed limit in harbour: no water-skiing. Contact Harbour Master Tel Fishguard (0348) 872881 No Charge.

Porthgain
Slipway
From Haverfordwest follow B 4330 and minor roads to coast: site is midway between St David's Hd and Strumble Hd. Steep concrete slipway onto rocky shore available for 2 hours either side HW suitable small powercraft only. No fuel, parking for car and trailer, toilets. Speed limit inshore. This is not an easy site. No Charge.

Abereiddy
Beach
From Haverfordwest follow B 4330 and minor roads to coast: site is about 10 miles north of St David's. Concrete slipway onto soft sand available at all states of tide for launching small craft that can be manhandled. Parking for car and trailer, toilets. **Caution:** there are rocky patches and strong currents offshore and large breakers build up on the beach, especially in onshore winds. Speed limit 8 knots inshore. No Charge.

St David's Head
Whitesand Bay
Follow B 4583 from St David's: access to site is through car park. Concrete slipway onto hard sand available at all states of tide and suitable small craft which can be manhandled. No fuel, parking for car and trailer (c), toilets. Speed limit 8 knots inshore: water-skiing permitted outside limits. There are strong currents and rocks offshore and breaking surf may be dangerous in onshore winds. No Charge.

Solva (St Bride's Bay)
Follow A 487 east from St David's: site is on north shore of bay and access is through car park. Concrete slipway available for 2/3 hours either side HW suitable small craft only. Fuel in village, parking for car and trailer, toilets. Speed limit 8 knots: no water-skiing. A very beautiful site which is often congested in summer. Charge.

Nolton Haven (St Bride's Bay)
Follow A 487 toward Haverfordwest turning off onto minor roads. Launching across shingle and sand beach available at all states of tide for small craft which can be manhandled. No fuel, parking for car and trailer, toilets. Speed limit 8 knots inshore: no water-skiing. Site sheltered except in westerlys: beware strong currents. No Charge.

Broad Haven (St Bride's Bay)
Follow B 4341 west from Haverfordwest. Small concrete slipway onto hard sand available at all states of tide but best for 3 hours either side HW for larger craft. Fuel, parking for car and trailer, toilets. Speed limit 8 knots inshore: no water-skiing. Dangerous surf in westerly winds. No Charge.

Martin's Haven (Broad Sound)
Follow B 4327 west from Haverfordwest turning off on minor roads: site is opposite Skomer Is. Concrete slipway onto pebble beach available for 2 hours either side HW suitable small craft only. No fuel, parking for car and trailer (c), toilets. Speed limit 8 knots: no water-skiing. Site is within Skomer Marine Reserve area where there are voluntary restrictions for craft and there are dangerous currents in the Sound. No Charge.

Milford Haven
One of the finest natural harbours in the world with over 24 miles of sheltered navigable water which is ideal for all watersports. The waterway is controlled by the Milford Haven Conservancy Board Tel Milford Haven(064 62) 3091/4 and is a major commercial port.

Dale (Milford Haven)
Dale Slipway
Follow B 4327 from Haverfordwest. Concrete slipway available for 4/5 hours either side HW suitable all craft. Fuel, parking for car and trailer (c), toilets, tractor, chandlery from Dale Sailing Co. Speed limit 6 knots close to beach. No Charge.

Gellyswick Bay (Milford Haven)
Follow main road through Milford Haven heading west: turn into Gellyswick Rd opposite the Esso garage; site is opposite Pembrokeshire YC. Wide concrete slipway onto hard sand available at all states of tide except LWS suitable all craft up to 40'LOA and 8'draught. Fuel, parking for car, leave trailer at PYC by arrangement (c), toilets and showers at club, chandlery from Dale Sailing Co. No speed limit: water-skiing permitted. Contact club for visitors' moorings and use of other facilities. No Charge.

Neyland (Milford Haven)
Follow A 4076 and A 477 from Haverfordwest: site is on north shore near Cleddau Bridge. Concrete slipway available at all states of tide except LWS and suitable all craft. Fuel, parking for car and trailer (c),toilets, chandlery from Westfield Marina. Speed limit. Great care is needed as the current can be dangerously strong here, especially at spring tides. No Charge.

Burton (Cleddau River)
Follow signs off A 477 on east side Cleddau Bridge. Concrete slipway onto gravel available at all states of tide. No fuel, limited parking (c), toilets, chandlery from Brunel Chandlery at Westfleet Marina. Speeed limit: water-skiing allowed (Burton Ski Club has facilities). Current can be strong here. No Charge.

Llangwm (Cleddau River)
Black Tar
Follow signs from A 4076 to Black Tar Point: site is 5 miles south of Haverfordwest. Concrete slipway available for 3 hours either side HW suitable small craft. No fuel, parking for car and trailer, toilets. Speed limit: no water-skiing. No Charge but donations to slip fund welcome.

Haverfordwest (W Cleddau River)
Old Quay
Follow A 40 west from Carmarthen: site is off Quay St. Concrete slipway available for 1 hour either side HW suitable small craft which can be manhandled. Fuel nearby, parking for car and trailer (c), toilets nearby. Speed limit: no water-skiing. Restricted headroom downriver. No Charge.

Landshipping Quay (E Cleddau River)
Foreshore
Turn of A 40 east of Haverfordwest onto A 4075 and follow signs. Steep concrete slipway onto gravel available for 2 hours either side HW suitable small craft which can be manhandled. No fuel, parking for car and trailer. No Charge.

Lawrenny (Cleddau River)
Lawrenny Yacht Station
Follow A 477 from Carmarthen turning right at Carew onto A 4075 then follow signs. Concrete slipway available at all states of tide suitable all craft. Fuel, parking for car and trailer (c), toilets, chandlery. Speed limit 4 knots in moorings. Further information Tel Carew(064 67) 212. Charge.

Hobbs Point (Milford Haven)
Pembroke Dock
Site is at end of A 477. Broad concrete slipway available at all states of tide except LWS suitable all craft. Fuel, parking for car and trailer (500yds), toilets, chandlery from Kelpie Boats. No Charge.

Pembroke Dock (Milford Haven)
Front Street
Follow A 477: site is at corner of Front St and Commercial Rd. Concrete slipway available for 3 hours either side HW. Fuel and parking for car and trailer nearby, chandlery from Kelpie Boats. No Charge.

Tenby Harbour (Carmarthen Bay)
Harbour Slipway
Follow A 40/A 477/A 478 from Carmarthen: site is adjacent SC. Concrete slipway onto hard sand available at all states of tide for craft up to 14'LOA. Fuel in town, limited parking for car and trailer (c), toilets nearby. Speed limit inshore. Site is very congested in summer: conditions outside harbour can be rough. Further information from the Harbour Master Tel Tenby(0834) 2717. No Charge.

Saundersfoot Harbour (Carmarthen Bay)
Harbour Slipway
Follow A 40/A 477 and B 4316 from Carmarthen. Concrete slipway onto hard sand available for 2½ hours either side HW or at all states of tide for dinghies. Fuel (1 mile), parking for car and trailer (c), toilets, chandlery from Jones & Teague Ltd. Speed limit 3 knots in harbour, 5 knots within 250yds of shore: water-skiing permitted in designated area. Further information from the Harbour Master Tel Saundersfoot(0834) 812094/813844. Harbour has good facilities but is crowded in summer: insurance cover is necessary before launching. Charge and harbour dues payable.

Laugharne (River Tay Estuary)
Follow A 40 west from Carmarthen turning south onto A 4066: site is by Castle. Launching over hard shingle beach available 2 hours either side HW and suitable small craft only. Fuel in village, parking for car and trailer, toilets. No Charge.

Llangain (Towy River)
Towy Boat Club
Follow B 4312 from Carmarthen: site is on Llanstephan Rd. Launching over shingle available for 2 hours either side HW suitable small craft only. No fuel, parking for car and trailer. Speed limit 5 knots. Charge.

Carmarthen (Towy River)
Carmarthen Boat Club, The Quay
On A 40. Steep concrete slipway available for 2 hours either side HW and suitable small powercraft only. Fuel from nearby garage, parking for car and trailer (c). Speed limit 5 knots: water-skiing permitted in designated area. Headroom restricted downriver. Charge.

Ferryside (Towy River)
River Towy Yacht Club
Follow A 484 south from Carmarthen turning off at Llandyfaelog and following signs. Concrete slipway available for 2 hours either side HW suitable all craft. Fuel by arrangement, parking for car and trailer (c), toilets. Speed limit 5 knots in moorings: water-skiing permitted in designated area. Best site in area: contact club for permission to use. Charge.

Kidwelly Quay
Folllow A 48 and A 484 from Carmarthen to site 1 mile south west of Kidwelly: access is via Station Rd and over railway line. Concrete slipway available for 2 hours either side HW and suitable all craft. Fuel in village, parking for car and trailer. This is a new facility. No Charge.

Burry Port Harbour
Harbour Slipway
Leave M 4 at junction 48 taking A 4138 and A 484 west. Four concrete slipways are available for 2½ hours either side HW and suitable all craft. Fuel, parking for car and trailer, toilets, chandlery from Burry Port Yacht Services: BPYC welcomes visitors. The bar at the entrance is dangerous in strong westerly winds. Speed limit 3 knots within harbour limits. Contact Superintendent Tel Burry Port(055 46) 758181. Charge.

Llanelli
Lledi Basin Slipway
Leave M4 at junction 48 taking A 4138: site is ½ mile S of town centre; access is via Queen Victoria Rd and Cambrian St turning right along track across open ground. Concrete slipway available at all states of tide. Fuel (¼ mile), parking for car and trailer. Speed limit. No Charge.

WEST GLAMORGAN

Mumbles (Swansea Bay)
Knab Site, Southend
Site is off main Mumbles to Swansea road (A 4067) and opposite Mumbles YC. Two concrete slipways, one available for 4 hours either side HW, the other at all times except for 1½ hours either side LWS and suitable all craft. Fuel (1 mile), parking for car and trailer (c), toilets (200yds), chandlery from Sailsport. Speed limit 4 knots in moorings. Temporary membership of YC available: contact Secretary Tel Swansea(0792) 369321. No Charge.

Swansea (Swansea Bay)
Swansea Yacht and Sub Aqua Club, Pocketts Wharf
From M 4 follow A 48 and A 483: site adjoins East Burrows Rd. Concrete slipway available for 3 hours either side HW suitable all craft up to 35'LOA. Diesel, parking for car and trailer (c), toilets, chandlery from Cambrian Small Boats. Speed limit 4 knots: no water-skiing. By prior arrangement only Tel Swansea(0792) 54863. Charge.

Swansea Yacht Haven (Swansea Bay)
Turn off M 4 and follow signs to Maritime Quarter off A 483 (Oystermouth Rd). Launching by travel hoist only from 0900-1700 into locked marina: lock gates open for 3½ hours either side HW. Fuel, parking for car and trailer, crane, toilets, chandlery from Cambrian Small Boats, full boatyard facilities on site. Speed limit 4 knots. Further information Tel Swansea(0792) 470310. Charge and harbour dues payable.

Port Talbot (Swansea Bay)
Aberavon Beach
Turn off M 4 at junction 41 and follow signs. Two concrete slipways onto beach available at all states of tide and suitable craft up to 20'LOA. Fuel, parking for car and trailer, toilets. Speed limit inshore. No Charge.

Porthcawl (Bristol Channel)
Harbour Slipway
Leave M 4 at junction 37 taking A 4229 and following signs to seafront. Access at top of slipway is restricted. Steep concrete slipway available for 3 hours either side HW suitable small craft. No fuel, parking for car and trailer, toilets. In bad weather a surge runs up the slipway and choppy conditions develop in E to SE winds. Contact Harbour Attendant Tel Porthcawl(065 671) 2756. Charge.

Penarth
Leave M 4 at junction 32 taking A 470 and B 1160. Concrete slipway available for 2 hours either side HW. Fuel in town, parking for car and trailer (c), toilets, chandlery from S & M Boat Services. Permit required for launching. Charge.

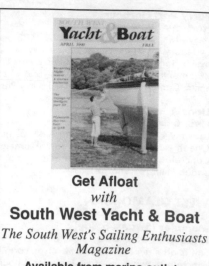

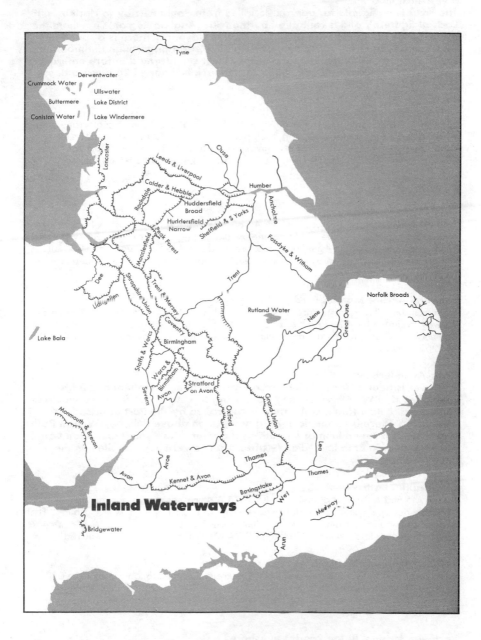

Inland Waterways

Tyne

Derwentwater

Crummock Water

Ullswater

Buttermere

Lake District

Conistan Water

Lake Windermere

Lancaster

Ouse

Leeds & Liverpool

Calder & Hebble

Humber

Rochdale

Ancholme

Huddersfield Broad

Huddersfield Narrow

Sheffield & S Yorks

Fossdyke & Witham

Macclesfield

Peak Forest

Dee

Trent

Shropshire Union

Trent & Mersey

Llangollen

Nene

Great Ouse

Norfolk Broads

Lake Bala

Rutland Water

Coventry

Staffs & Worcs

Birmingham

Worcs & Birmingham

Severn

Stratford on Avon

Oxford

Grand Union

Monmouth & Brecon

Avon

Avon

Thames

Lea

Kennet & Avon

Thames

Basingstoke

Wey

Medway

Bridgewater

Arun

RIVER SITES

River Ancholme

The river is navigable for approx 25 miles from South Ferriby to Harlem Hill Lock at Snitterby and is controlled by the NRA (Anglian Region)* to whom the appropriate navigation fee should be paid in advance. There is a speed limit of 7mph on the river, with a limit of 4mph in operation through the moorings at Sth Ferriby and Brigg. The lock-keeper must be informed before entering the river Tel Sth Ferriby(0652) 635224: the lock is manned 24 hours a day from 1st April - 30th Oct.

Clapson Marina, Red Lane

Turn off A 1077 Scunthorpe to Barton Rd at Sth Ferriby Sluice. Launching by crane during working hours only, suitable all craft. Fuel, parking for car and trailer (c), toilets, chandlery. Speed limit 7mph. Site also gives access to tidal R Humber. Check for availability Tel Barton upon Humber(0652) 635620. Charge and licence required.

River Arun

Swan Corner, Pulborough

Turn off A 29 Bognor Rd at junction with A 283: site is beside bridge on N bank of river and on the other side of the road from the Swan Inn. Steep concrete slipway with snatch block available during daylight hours near HW and suitable boats up to 15'LOA. Fuel in village, limited parking nearby, or at station (c) ($\frac{1}{4}$ mile), toilets in village. Speed limit $6\frac{1}{2}$ knots on river. No Charge.

Ship and Anchor Marina, Ford

From Arundel follow signs to Ford: site is on west bank of river after station. Concrete slipway available for 4 hours either side HW. No fuel, parking for car and trailer, toilets and chandlery, pub, restaurant and camp site. Check for availability Tel Yapton(0243) 551262. Charge.

River Avon (Bristol)

The river is tidal as far as Hanham Lock and between Hanham and Bath is controlled by BW with whom any boat using this stretch of the river should be registered. Below Hanham the river is controlled by the Port of Bristol Authority*. There is no public right of navigation above Pulteney Weir in Bath and there is a speed limit of 4 knots on the river. The Kennet and Avon Canal joins the river in Bath immediately after Bath Lower Lock. For sites on the canal see page 138.

Newbridge, Bath

Follow A 4 and A 39 west of Bath: site is where A 4 crosses river. Concrete slipway available during daylight hours and suitable craft up to 23'LOA and with 3' draught. Fuel nearby, parking for car and trailer, chandlery from Bath and Newbridge Marine Services adjacent. Further information Tel Bath(0225) 24301. Charge and licence required.

Saltford Marina, The Shallows

Situated on A 4 between Bristol and Bath. Concrete slipway available daily from 0900-1700 or at other times by arrangement Tel Saltford (0225) 872226 and suitable for craft up to 25'LOA. Fuel, parking for car and trailer, toilets, chandlery on site. Charge and licence required.

Portavon Marina, Bitton Road, Keynsham

Leave A 4 at Keynsham and follow A 4175 over bridge. Concrete slipway available daily from 0900-1730 by prior arrangement Tel Bitton(0272) 861626. Fuel, parking for car and trailer, toilets, chandlers. Charge and licence required.

114

Jondeblin Marine, Broadmead Lane, Keynsham
Turn off A 4 at Keynsham west of Bath. Steep concrete slipway with rails available by prior arrangement Tel(0272) 861168 and suitable craft up to 23'LOA and with 3' draught. Diesel, parking for car and trailer (c). Charge and licence required.

Chequers Inn, Hanham
Turn off A 431 at Hanham and follow minor roads to lock. Steep concrete and wood slipway suitable craft up to 23'LOA and with 3' draught available during daylight hours by arrangement Tel Hanham(0272) 674242. Fuel, parking for car and trailer, toilets. Charge and licence required.

River Avon (Warwickshire)
Between Offenham Ferry and Alveston Sluice, the limit of navigation, the river is controlled by the Upper Avon Navigation Trust* and there is a speed limit of 4mph. Between Offenham Ferry and Tewkesbury the river is controlled by the Lower Avon Navigation Trust* and there is a 6mph speed limit. The River Avon joins the River Severn a short distance below Mythe Bridge in Tewkesbury.

Stratford Marina Ltd, Clopton Bridge
Leave M 5 at junction 6 taking A 422 east to Stratford-upon-Avon: in town follow one-way system, taking first left after passing the Moat House International Hotel. Concrete slipway available daily from 0830-2030 (summer) and 0900-1700 (winter) suitable dinghies and powerboats. Fuel, parking for car and trailer (c), toilets, chandlery and boatyard facilities on site. Further information Tel Stratford-upon-Avon(0789) 69669. Charge.

Bidford Boats, 4 The Pleck, Bidford-on-Avon
Follow A 439 west from Stratford-upon-Avon: site is next to Bidford Garages. Concrete slipway available 0900-2000 in the summer suitable craft up to 25'LOA. Petrol, parking for car and trailer (c). Further information Tel Stratford-upon-Avon(0789) 773205. Charge.

Barton Cruisers, Welford Road, Barton
Follow A 439 west from Stratford-upon-Avon turning left over the river onto the B 4085 Honeybourne Rd at Bidford-on-Avon: take first left tuning to Barton and site is on left. Concrete slipway into min 3'water available 0900-2000 daily and suitable all craft. Fuel ($\frac{1}{2}$ mile), parking for car and trailer (c), chandlery. Further information Tel(0789) 772003. Charge.

Evesham Marina (Fenmatch Ltd)
Leave M 5 at junction 7 following A 44 east to Evesham: access is via Kings Road. Concrete slipway available 0900-1700. Fuel, parking for car and trailer (c), toilets, chandlery. Further information Tel Evesham (0386) 2338. Charge.

Sankey Marine, Worcester Road, Evesham
Leave M 5 at junction 7 following A 44 east to Pershore then take B 4083/B 4084 east. Concrete slipway available during daylight hours. Fuel, parking for car and trailer (c), toilets, chandlery. Further information Tel Evesham(0386) 2338. Charge.

J Sanders, Pensham Road, Pershore
Follow M 5 turning off at junction 7 onto A 44 to Pershore: at Pershore new bridge turn right then fork right and the entrance drive will be seen on the right. Steep concrete slipway available 0900-1300 and 1400-1800 and suitable craft up to 25'LOA. Fuel, parking for car and trailer (c), toilets, chandlery. Further information Tel Pershore(0386) 552765. Charge.

Tewkesbury Marina, Bredon Road
Leave M 5 at junction 9 taking A 438 west, then A 38 and B 4080. Gantry crane available during weekday working hours Tel Tewkesbury(0684) 293737. Fuel, parking for car and trailer (c), toilets and showers, chandlery. Charge.

River Dee

Dee Fords, Sandy Lane
From Chester follow B 5130, 1½ miles south. Concrete slipway available at all times. No fuel, parking for car and trailer (c), toilets, chandlery from Chester Boat Chandlers, 31 Christleton Road. The river is navigable from Chester to Farndon and all mechanically or electrically propelled boats must be registered with the Director of Environmental Health, 16 White Friars. There is a speed limit of 6mph. Charge and licence required.

River Humber see page 70.

River Lea
There is a speed limit of 4mph on the river which is navigable from Limehouse Basin or Bow Locks where the tidal Thames can be entered to Hertford and a BW licence is required for navigation. The Lea Valley has been designated a regional park and is administered by the Lea Valley Park Authority*.

Broxbourne Meadows
Turn off A 10 north of Cheshunt onto A 1170, turning off south of the traffic lights into Mill Lane. Concrete slipway into 3' water available daily 0900-1800 Apr-Oct suitable craft up to 16'LOA: obtain key from Warden. Fuel, parking for car and trailer (c), toilets, boatyard facilities from Broxbourne Boat Centre. Further information Tel Hoddesdon (0992) 461951. Charge and licence required.

Stanstead Abbots Marina, South Street
Turn off A 10 south of Ware onto A 414 and into South St. Concrete slipway into 4' water suitable small craft available 0900-1700 daily. Diesel, parking for car and trailer (c), crane for hire, toilets, chandlery and boatyard facilities. Further information Tel Ware(0920) 870499. Charge and licence required.

Hayes-Allen Boatyard, Rye House Quay, Hoddesdon
Turn off A 10 at Hoddesdon exit and follow signs to Rye Park. Concrete slipway into 3' water available daily during daylight working hours from Easter to end of October and suitable craft up to 30'LOA (no powerboats). No fuel, parking for car and trailer (c), toilets, chandlery and repairs. Low bridges restrict craft with masts. Further information Tel Hoddesdon(0992) 460888. Charge and licence required.

Springfield Marina (Lee Valley Marina), Clapton
Turn off A 107. Concrete slipway available 0900-1700 weekdays, 0900-1300 weekends. Fuel, parking for car and trailer, crane and winch for hire, toilets, boatyard facilities. Further information Tel 081 806 1717. Charge and licence required.

River Medway
Above Allington Lock the river is not tidal and is controlled by the NRA (Southern Region)*. All vessels using the navigation must be registered. There is a speed limit of 5 knots. See page 53 for sites on the tidal Medway.

Allington Marina, Maidstone
Leave M 20 at junction 6 following the A 229 south and A 20 west: turn right down Castle Rd opposite the garage. Concrete slipway into 6' water available during daylight hours and suitable small craft. Fuel, parking for car and trailer (c), toilets, crane, chandlery. Check for availability Tel Maidstone(0622) 752057. Charge and licence required.

Bow Bridge Marina, Bow Bridge, Wateringbury Road
Turn off A 26 Tonbridge to Maidstone road at Wateringbury crossroads, going down the hill and over the level crossing, then taking the first left turning. Concrete slipway with winch into min 2½' water available 0900-1800 in the summer and suitable all craft up to 30'LOA. Fuel, parking for car and trailer (c), crane, toilets, telephone and chandlery. Further information Tel (0622) 812802. Charge and licence required.

Medway Wharf Marina, Bow Bridge, Wateringbury

Turn off A 26 Tonbridge to Maidstone road at Wateringbury crossroads and take first right turn after crossing the bridge by the railway station. Steep concrete slipway into min 2½' water available 0830-dusk and suitable all craft: launching is by yard staff only. Fuel, parking for car and trailer (c), crane, winch, toilets, telephone. Check for availability Tel (0622) 813927. Charge and licence required.

Yalding

Turn off B 2015 onto B 2162 between Wateringbury and E Peckam: site is opposite ICI Plant. Steep concrete slipway into min 2½' water available by prior arrangement only and suitable craft up to 25'LOA. Fuel (1 mile), no parking on site but car park, boatyard and café at end of Hampstead Lane (½ mile) near lock-keeper's office. Speed limit 5 knots: no water-skiing. Contact NRA (Southern Region) Office in Vale Rd, Tonbridge Tel (0732) 364922 for permission to launch. Charge and licence required.

Lower Castle Field, Tonbridge

Follow the A 26 into Tonbridge High St turning left after the Castle into Castle St and following the Slade to the riverside car park: access is via narrow and often congested streets and the car park has a height restriction of 6'. Concrete slipway into min 3'water available during daylight hours and suitable craft up to 20'LOA. Fuel (½ mile), parking for car and trailer (c), toilets, telephone. Licences are available from the TIC, the Castle or the Angel Centre. No Charge but licence required.

River Nene

The river is tidal for 25 miles as far as the Dog-in-a-Doublet lock and sluice, 5 miles below Peterborough and is controlled by the Port of Wisbech Authority*. The lock is open daily from 0730 - sunset: it is advisable to telephone the lock-keeper in advance Tel Peterborough(0733) 202219 to make arrangements. Above the lock, the river, is navigable to Northampton and thence to the Grand Union Canal via the Northampton Branch. The river which is controlled by the NRA (Anglian Region)*, is important because it links the Grand Union Canal to the Middle Level Navigations and the sea. There is a speed limit of 7mph with a derestricted stretch of water 1 mile downstream of Peterborough. All craft must pay the appropriate navigation fees in advance.

Billing Aquadrome, Little Billing

Leave M 1 at junction 15 taking A 508 and A 45 east: site is 3 miles from Northampton. Two concrete slipways available 24 hours a day Tel Northampton(0604) 408181. Fuel, parking for car and trailer, toilets and showers, chandlery. Charge and licence required.

Wellingborough Upper Lock

Follow A 45 east from Northampton: site is on left bank, downstream of the upper lock and access is via Turnells Mill Lane. Concrete slipway available during daylight hours. No parking on site, toilets (¼ mile). No Charge and licence required.

Mill Marina, Thrapston

Follow A 604 west from Huntingdon, taking A 605 south in Thrapston towards Raunds: site is signposted. Concrete slipway into min 2'water available during daylight working hours and suitable all craft up to 20'/25'LOA depending on the state of the river. Fuel, parking for car and trailer (c), toilets, telephone, caravan park and coarse fishing available on site: nearest yard facilities at Oundle Marine (15 miles). Further information Tel Thrapston(080 12) 2850. Charge and licence required.

Oundle Marina, Barnwell Road

Follow A 605 west from A 1. Concrete slipway available from 0900-1800 or by arrangement Tel Oundle(0832) 72762. Fuel, parking for car and trailer (c), toilets, showers, chandlers. Speed limit 5mph. Charge and licence required.

Drake Towage, Crab Marsh, Wisbech

Follow A 47 to main port area, past ship-turning area. Concrete slipway available from 2 hours before HW to 1 hour after HW suitable all craft up to 70'LOA. Fuel, parking for car and trailer, crane, winch, toilets. Speed limit: water-skiing allowed downriver at Sutton Bridge. Further information Tel Wisbech(0945) 589539. Charge.

Middle Level Navigations

These channels connect the River Nene and the River Great Ouse and are controlled by the NRA (Anglian Region)* and the Middle Level Commissioners*. Pleasure craft are not required to pay a licence fee but visitors should register with the lock-keeper at Stanground or Salters Lode when entering the system. There is a max speed limit of 5mph with the exception of Kings Dyke and Well Ck where the limit is 4mph.

C T & P Fox Marina, 10 Marina Drive, March

Leave A 141 at March roundabout taking Turves exit and keep bearing left into Marina Drive. Concrete slipway suitable all craft. Fuel, parking for car and trailer (c), boatyard facilities. Speed limit 5mph. Use by arrangement only Tel March(0354) 52770. Charge.

Great Ouse

The river is now navigable from Bedford to King's Lynn and is controlled by the NRA (Anglian Region)*: all craft must pay the appropiate navigation fee in advance. There is a speed limit of 6 knots unless otherwise specified. The navigation authority for the lower reaches of the river and seaward approaches to King's Lynn is the King's Lynn Conservancy Board*.

Priory Marina (Harry Kitchener Marine Ltd) Bedford

Turn off A 1 onto A 428: access is via Barkers Lane on outskirts of Bedford. Concrete slipway into min 4' water available from 0830-1730 daily Tel Bedford(0234) 51931/3. Fuel, parking for car and trailer (c), toilets, chandlery, moorings and servicing facilities. Charge and licence required.

Crosshall Marine, St Neots

Follow signs to St Neots Golf Club: access to site is through club car park and width is restricted to 7'4". Gentle concrete slipway available 0900-1930 daily and suitable small craft only. Fuel, parking for car and trailer, crane operated by yard staff if required, toilets, chandlery. Further information Tel Huntingdon(0480) 72763. Charge and licence required.

Buckden Marina, Buckden

On A1 south of Huntingdon turn east in Buckden. Concrete slipway available daily from 0800-1800 Tel Huntingdon(0480) 810355. Fuel, parking for car and trailer (c), toilets, chandlery, moorings. Charge and licence required.

Huntingdon

Follow ring road round town, turning off to follow signs to St Ives, after 50yds cross over into car park by the river: site is downstream of Purvis Marine. Concrete slipway with sharp drop at end into min 3'water available during daylight hours and suitable craft up to 20'LOA. Fuel (½ mile), parking for car and trailer. No Charge but licence required.

Hartford Marina, Banks End, Wyton

Site is on A 1123 between Huntingdon and St Ives. Concrete slipway available from 0900-1700 daily Tel St Ives(0480) 54677/8. Fuel, parking for car and trailer (c), toilets, chandlery and all marina facilities. Charge and licence required.

Town Quay, St Ives

Turn off eastern bypass road at the Meadow Lane junction: site is at the quay downstream of the old bridge. Concrete slipway into approx 3'water available at all times and suitable small craft. Fuel nearby, parking for car and trailer (c), toilets, chandlery from The Boathaven. No Charge but licence required.

The Boathaven (L H Jones & Son), St Ives
Site is beside the St Ives bypass. Concrete slipway available during daylight hours Tel St Ives(0480) 494040. Fuel, parking for car and trailer (c), toilets, chandlery. Charge and licence required.

Westview Marina, High Street, Earith
Follow A 1123 east from Huntingdon to Earith. Concrete slipway available from 0900-1730 Tel Ramsey(0487) 841627. Fuel, parking for car and trailer (c), toilets and showers, chandlery. Charge and licence required.

Hermitage Marina, Earith
Follow A 1123 east from Huntingdon. Concrete slipway available from 0730-1800 daily Tel Ramsey(0487) 840994. Fuel, parking for car and trailer (c), toilets, chandlery. Charge and licence required.

Bridge Boatyard, Bridge Road, Ely
In Ely take A 142 towards Newmarket: site is near rail crossing. Steep concrete slipway available during daylight hours suitable craft up to 32'LOA. Fuel, parking for car and trailer (c), tractor available, toilets, boatyard facilities. Further information Tel Ely(0353) 663726. Charge and licence required.

Ely Marina, Waterside
From Cambridge follow A 10 north to Ely and signs to river. Concrete slipway available during daylight hours suitable craft up to 20'LOA. Fuel, parking for car and trailer (c), toilets and showers, chandlery. Further information Tel Ely(0353) 664622. Charge and licence required.

Waterside, Ely
From A 142 turn into Broad Street and follow signs to river. Launching over shingle available during daylight hours and suitable small craft only. Fuel, parking for car and trailer, other facilities at marina nearby. No Charge but licence required.

Denver
Follow A 10 north to Downham Market, taking A 1507 to Denver and following signs in village to Denver Sluice: this is the tidal limit of the river. The site is upriver of the sluice, beside the Jenyns Arms Inn. Concrete slipway available at all times and suitable small craft only: obtain the key from the lock-keeper Tel Downham Market(0366) 382340. No fuel, parking for car and trailer. Charge and licence required.

Common Staithe Quay, King's Lynn
Follow A 10 north to King's Lynn: site is on tidal river. Concrete slipway available for 2 hours either side HW and suitable all craft. Fuel, parking for car and trailer (c), toilets, chandlery from Austin Fields. At LW thick mud is exposed. No Charge.

River Ouse (Yorkshire)
The river is tidal to Naburn Lock and commercial traffic still reaches York. The Ouse and Foss Navigation Trustees control the river from 2 miles south of Linton Lock to Skelton Bridge, Goole. Contact the River Manager, Naburn Lock Tel Escrick(090 487) 229 or Selby(0757) 708949 for information. No licence fee but there is a charge for passing Naburn Lock.

Boroughbridge Marina (Tower Marine Services) Boroughbridge
Turn off A 1 onto B 6265: access is via Roecliffe Lane. Concrete slipway 18'wide with 1:6 incline available during daylight hours and suitable craft up to 40'LOA. Fuel at town quay, parking for car and trailer (c), toilets and showers, chandlery. Check for availability Tel Boroughbridge(0423) 322011. Speed limit 4mph. Charge.

Acaster Malbis
Turn off A 64 Leeds to York road at Copmanthorpe. Concrete slipway with winch and rollers. Fuel nearby, parking for car and trailer, toilets, chandlers. Obtain permission on site. Speed limit 4mph. Further information Tel York(0904) 706819. Charge.

York Marine Services Ltd, Ferry Lane, Bishopthorpe

Turn off the A 64 at Bishopthorpe, 2 miles south of York. Steep concrete slipway available 0900-1800 daily and suitable craft up to 23'LOA: tractor assisted launch available. Diesel on site, petrol nearby, parking for car and trailer, toilets and showers (c), restaurant, camp site, chandlery and visitors' moorings. Speed limit 6 knots. Further information Tel York(0904) 704442. Charge.

River Severn

Between Gloucester and Stourport-on-Severn the river is controlled by BW and boats using the river are required to be registered and licensed. Speed limit is 6mph above Kempsey and 8mph below: no water-skiing.

Seaborne Yacht Co Ltd, Court Meadow, Kempsey

From M 5 take M 50 and A 38 north: site is 2 miles south of Worcester. Concrete slipway with trolley on rails available at all times but subject to the state of the river. Fuel, parking for car and trailer, toilets, chandlery. Further information Tel Worcester(0905) 820295. Charge and licence required.

Upton Marina, East Waterside, Upton-upon-Severn

Follow A 38 north from Gloucester, turning onto A 4104 north of Tewkesbury. Steep concrete slipway which levels off into shallow water available daily from 0830-1300 & 1400-1730: launcher should seek advice Tel Upton-upon-Severn(06846) 3111. Fuel, parking for car and trailer (c), toilets, chandlery. Charge and licence required.

Lower Lode Hotel, Forthampton

From A 438 Tewkesbury to Ledbury road turn into village and follow signs to Lower Lode: site is disused ferry slipway adjacent to hotel and access is via a narrow lane. Gentle slipway into min 3'water available at all times and suitable craft up to 26'LOA: jet skies are not allowed. Fuel (3 miles), parking for car and trailer, toilets, telephone. Permission to launch must be obtained from the owner of the hotel. Charge and licence required.

River Thames

The controlling authority for navigation on the non-tidal part of the river from Teddington to Cricklade is the NRA (Thames Region)* with whom boats intending to use this part of the river should be registered and licensed. All boats should navigate in the fairway, keeping to the right- hand side of the channel and proceed at slow speed (max permitted speed 7 knots).

Launching is available at the following yards as specified and may be available at other private sites on request. Most boatyards on the river are very busy at weekends with boat hire and do not welcome casual launching: it is advisable to check for the availability of sites before setting off.

Oxford Cruisers, Eynsham

From A 40 west of Oxford, turn off to Eynsham and follow B 4044 to Farmoor: there is a fairly narrow toll bridge on this approach, larger craft may need to find an alternative route. Concrete slipway into approx 3'water available 0830-1800 daily and suitable all craft. Fuel, parking for car and trailer (c), toilets, telephone. Tractor, crane, winch, boat lift (12 ton), chandlery and yard facilities available on site. Further information Tel Oxford(0865) 881698. Charge and licence required.

Benson Cruisers, Benson

On A 423 Henley to Oxford road near junction with B 4009, just upriver of Benson Lock on the east bank. Concrete slipway into 12' water available 0830-1800 (summer), 0900-1600 (winter) suitable all craft. Fuel, parking for car and trailer (c), toilets, chandlery, shop and restaurant on site. Further information Tel Wallingford(0491) 38304. Charge and licence required.

Sheridan UK, The Boatyard, Moulsford
On A 329 south of Wallingford on the west bank and just upstream of Beetle and
Wedge Hotel: access is limited by small bridge. Concrete slipway into 3½' water
available during daylight hours when not in use by yard staff. Petrol from garage
nearby, parking for car and trailer (c), crane, winch, chandlery and boatyard facilities on
site. Further information Tel Cholsey(0491) 652085. Charge and licence required.

Val Wyatt Marine Ltd, Willow Lane, Wargrave
Turn off M 4/A 423(M) at junction 9 following A 4 and A 321. Concrete slipway available
daily 0800-1700. Fuel, parking for car and trailer (c), toilets, chandlery. By prior
arrangement only Tel Wargrave(0735 22) 3211. Charge and licence required.

Hobbs and Sons Ltd, Wargrave Road, Henley-on-Thames
Turn off M 4 at junction 9 and follow A 423(M) and A 423 towards Henley: site is ⅓ mile
outside town on east bank of river. Concrete slipway 9' wide into 3' water. Fuel, parking
for car and trailer (c), toilets, chandlery. Charge and licence required.

Hurley Caravan and Camping Park (Hurley Farms Limited), Hurley
Leave M 4 at junction 9 taking A 423(M) then A 423 turning off to Hurley and north into
the High Street by East Arms pub. At village green, ½ mile further on, take left fork and
entrance to riverside car park is 50 yds on left. Slipway into 3' water available 0800-
dusk (Mar 1st-Nov 1st) suitable craft up to 20'LOA. Fuel, parking for car and trailer (c),
toilets, chandlery and boatyard facilities from Peter Freebody's. Charge and licence
required.

Harleyford Marina, Marlow
Leave M 40 at junction 4 taking A 404 and A 4155: site is on north bank near Temple
Lock. Launching by boat lift for craft up to 15 tons available by prior arrangement only
Tel Marlow(06284) 71368. Charge and licence required.

Bray Marina, Monkey Is Lane, Bray
Leave M 4 at junction 9 taking A 308 towards Windsor. Launching by crane from 0900-
1700 (mon - fri only) for craft up to 8 tons. Fuel, parking for car and trailer (c), toilets,
chandlery. By prior arrangement only Tel Maidenhead(0628) 23654. Charge and licence
required.

Windsor Marina, Maidenhead Road, Oakley Green, Windsor
Leave M 4 at junction 9 taking A 308 towards Windsor. Concrete slipway into 3' water
for boats up to 20'LOA with liftable outboard engines, available daily 0830-1730. Fuel,
parking for car and trailer (c), toilets, chandlery and full marina facilities. Further
information Tel Windsor(075 35) 53911. Charge and licence required.

Racecourse Yacht Basin, Maidenhead Road, Windsor
Leave M 4 at junction 9 taking A 308: turn left after Windsor Lad pub. Concrete slipway
available at all times. Fuel, parking for car and trailer (c), toilets, chandlery. Further
information Tel Windsor(075 35) 51501. Charge and licence required.

Penton Hook Marina, Staines Lane, Chertsey
Leave M 25 at junction 11: site is off A 320 opposite Thorpe Park. Concrete slipway
available daily 0900-1700. Fuel, parking for car and trailer (c), toilets, chandlery. Further
information Tel Chertsey(093 28) 62145. Charge and licence required.

Chertsey Meads Marine, Chertsey
Leave M 25 at junction 11, taking A 319 St Peters Way, Chertsey Rd, Fordwater Rd and
turning into Mead Lane. Steep concrete slipway into approx 3'water available 0900-
1800 (other times by arangement only) and suitable all craft. Petrol nearby, diesel on
site, parking for car and trailer (c), crane and winch operated by yard staff if required,
toilets, telephone and limited chandlery. Further information Tel Chertsey(093 28) 64699.
Charge and licence required.

Nauticalia, Ferry Lane, Shepperton
From A 3 take A 244 to Walton-on-Thames, crossing Walton Bridge and turning left onto
B 375. Slipway available during normal business hours into 7'water and suitable craft up
to 42'LOA. Fuel, parking for car and trailer (c), winch, toilets, chandlery and boatyard
facilities on site. Further information Tel Walton-on-Thames(0932) 244396. Charge and
licence required.

Gibbs Marine Sales, Russel Rd, Shepperton
Leave M 25 at junction 11 taking A 317 and A 244 across the bridge: site is in Russel Rd
opposite The Ship. Concrete slipway into min 5'water available 0900-1800(mon-sat),
1000-1800(sun) and suitable all craft. Fuel, parking for car and trailer. Further
information Tel Walton(093 22) 20926. Charge and licence required.

Walton Marine Sales, Walton Bridge, Walton-on-Thames
Leave M 25 at junction 11 taking A 317: site is just downstream of Walton Br. Concrete
slipway for boats up to 23'LOA available daily 1030-1700. Fuel, parking for car and
trailer nearby (c), toilets, chandlery, crane available. Further information Tel Walton-on-
Thames(0932) 226266. Charge and licence required.

Bridge Marine, Thames Meadow, Shepperton
Leave M 25 at junction 11 taking A 317 and A 244 across the bridge. Concrete slipway
into 6' water available 1000-1700 suitable craft up to 30'LOA. Petrol from garage,
parking for car and trailer (c), toilets nearby, chandlery from Gibbs Chandlery, boatyard
facilities and engineer on site, tractor available for assistance. Further information Tel
Walton on Thames(0932) 245126. Speed limit 4 knots. Charge and licence required.

Shepperton Marina, Shepperton
Turn off M 25 at junction 11 taking A 317 to Walton-on-Thames then follow A 244 over
bridge: site is downstream of bridge on north bank. Launching by boat lift only for craft
up to 20 tons available by prior arrangement only Tel Walton-on-Thames(0932)
247427. Charge and licence required.

Toughs Shipyard Ltd, Manor Road, Teddington
From Sunbury follow A 308 east and A 311/312 to Teddington: site is on west bank of
river downstream of the Anglers Hotel. Slipway into approx 8' water available during
normal working hours. Fuel, parking for car and trailer, crane (15 tons), launching trolley
up to 20 tons, toilets, chandlery from Suntest Ltd. Check for avalability Tel 081 977
4494. Charge and licence requied.

**In addition to these sites there are a number of public launching sites
available to the public as follows: while launching from most of these sites is
free, craft must still be registered with the NRA (Thames Region)*.**

Radcot - follow A 4095 north from Faringdon and over bridge. Small boats can be
launched with permission beside The Swan Inn on the north bank of the river and
downstream of the bridge.

Bablock Hythe - small boats can be launched from the ferry slip on either riverbank
with permission from the Ferry Inn on the west bank Tel Oxford(0865) 882207: do not
obstruct the pedestrian ferry.

Oxford - launch from ramp upstream of Donnington Bridge on the east bank of the
river: access is via Meadow Lane. The site gives access to the river downstream of Folly
Bridge and just below the mouth of the River Cherwell. Parking is limited on site.

Abingdon - turn off A 34, taking A 415. Small boats can be launched from ramp at St
Helen's Wharf, near St Helen's Church.

Clifton Hampden - follow A 415 east from Abingdon, crossing over bridge: small boats
can be launched near the Barley Mow Inn on the east bank of the river and upstream of
the bridge.

Cholsey - follow A 329 south from Wallingford, turning left into Papist Way just after Fair Mile Hospital. Small boats can be launched from the hard at the end of the road.

Moulsford - follow A 329 south from Wallingford: site is at old ferry crossing beside the Beetle and Wedge Hotel Tel Cholsey(0491) 651381.

Pangbourne - follow A 329 north west from Reading: launch from site adjacent to the Swan Hotel, just above Whitchurch Lock and on the south bank of the river. Ask permission at the hotel Tel Pangbourne(07357) 3199.

Purley - turn off A 329 crossing over railway line and into Mapledurham Drive which leads to the lock: site is upriver of the lock on the west bank.

Reading - follow A 4155 to Caversham Bridge: site is immediately upstream of the bridge on the south bank of the river.

Wargrave - turn off A 4 onto A 321: small craft only can be launched from the end of Ferry Lane beside The Greyhound.

Henley-on-Thames - leave A 4 at Maidenhead and follow A 423, crossing over the bridge and turning right: launch at end of Wharf Lane, downstream of the bridge on the west bank.

Aston Ferry - follow signs off A 423 for south bank or A 4155 for north bank: launch from disused ferry site on either bank.

Medmenham - follow signs off A 4155: site is at end of road which leads down to the river opposite The Dog and Badger Inn.

Marlow - turn into High St from A 4155, turning left at end of street into Station Rd then right into St Peter's St. Concrete slipway into min 4'water suitable dinghies and small cabin cruisers. Fuel, parking for car and trailer, toilets, telephone.

Cookham - follow A 4094 to Cookham, turning into Odney Lane opposite the High St and then turning left immediately: site is adjacent to the Ferry Inn downstream of the bridge. Concrete slipway onto shingle into min 3½' water available at all times and suitable small, open powerboats and dinghies. Fuel, parking for car and trailer, toilets, telephone.

Bray - follow B 3028 from Maidenhead: launch from end of Ferry Road beside the Waterside Inn.

Laleham - take B 376 from Staines and launch from end of road beside the Three Horseshoes.

Weybridge - launch from slipway adjacent to Weybridge Marine Ltd at the junction of Walton Lane and Thames Street: site is near the mouth of the River Wey.

Shepperton - launch from Shepperton Village Wharf: site is at end of road by Anchor Inn in Church Square.

Walton-on-Thames - launch from Cowey Sale upriver of Walton Bridge on the south bank or from Walton Wharf further downstream beside the Anglers Hotel in Manor Road.

Sunbury - launch from Lower Hampton Road just upriver of Sunbury Court and opposite Sunbury Court Island.

West Moseley - launch from Hurst Park turning off Hurst Road (A 3050) into Sadlers Ride: site is upriver of Hampton Court Bridge and opposite Garrick's Ait.

East Molesey - launch at drawdock.

Thames Ditton - turn off A 309 into Summer Road and launch by the Swan Hotel: site is opposite Thames Ditton Island.

Kingston-upon-Thames - follow A 308 to Kingston Bridge: launch from Thameside on east bank downriver of the bridge and adjacent to Turks Boatyard.

Teddington - launch at drawdock.

Access to many of these sites may be congested and parking in such built up areas is always likely to prove difficult. It is advisable to check out the site first to ensure suitability and to establish local conditions.

Below Teddington Lock, the river is tidal and controlled by The Port of London Authority*. Pleasure craft should keep clear of commercial vessels and beware strong currents which may carry them into moored barges. Speed should be limited to prevent excess wash: above Wandsworth Bridge there is a speed limit of 8 knots. It is strongly recommended that before launching at any of the sites listed below, visitors should contact the Harbour Master (see below) for the latest information regarding navigation on the river and availability of sites, which may sometimes be obstructed by commercial craft.

Upper Section (Twickenham - Woolwich)Tel 071 481 0720
Lower Section (Woolwich - Sea Reach)Tel 0474 567684

Teddington - launch from slipway at end of Ferry Rd just downriver of the lock: get key to gate from Tough Bros at Teddington Wharf. Best launching near HW: at LW site is very muddy.

Twickenham - launch from hard gravel foreshore at end of Church Lane, on Embankment or from ramp opposite White Swan Inn, Riverside: access to these sites is narrow and launching is possible at all times except for 1 hour either side HW.

Ham - turn off A 307 following lane to Ham landing: this is a popular site and may be congested: site is adjacent public car park.

Petersham - turn off A 307 on sharp bend into River Lane: site is 1 mile upriver of Richmond Bridge and best launching is near HW.

Richmond - launch from drawdock at bottom of Water Lane just downriver of Richmond Bridge: site is often congested.

Isleworth - turn off A 315 into Park Rd: site is adjacent London Apprentice Inn. Launch from concrete slipway for approx 2 hours either side HW suitable craft up to 40'LOA and 10' wide. Fuel, parking for car and trailer, toilets, telephone: chandlery, crane and all yard facilities from Brent Marine, Brentford.

Kew Bridge - launch from drawdock adjacent to bridge on north bank of the river and downstream of the bridge: site is very muddy at low water.

Kew - launch from Grove Park drawdock at the end of Grove Park Road adjacent to Bason & Arnold's yard, immediately downriver of Kew railway bridge.

Mortlake - launch at the Ship drawdock at the end of Ship Lane off the Lower Richmond Rd and downriver of Chiswick Bridge: park well above tidal limit as road may flood.

Barnes - launch at Small Profits drawdock off Lonsdale Rd: best near HW.

124

Chiswick - launch from Chiswick Church drawdock at the end of Church St or from the drawdock 200yds downstream at HW.

Hammersmith - launch from drawdock downriver of the bridge.

Putney - launch at drawdock immediately upriver of bridge and opposite boathouses on the Embankment at any state of tide or downriver of the bridge from end of Brewhouse St, a turning off Putney Bridge Rd.

Battersea - launch from drawdock near Church: access is from Battersea Church Road.

Isle of Dogs   launch from Newcastle drawdock or Johnsons drawdock at any state of tide, both accessible from Saunders Ness road: or launch from site on the Samuda Housing estate on eastern side of Isle of Dogs off the Manchester Road at slipway available for approx 3 hours either side HW with parking available for car and trailer.

Greenwich - launch from Point drawdock at the end of Drawdock Rd, a turning off Tunnell Avenue which leads to the Blackwall Tunnel: or launch from Bugsby's Hole Causeway at the end of River Way, a turning off Blackwall Lane which forks off Tunnel Avenue.

Woolwich - launch from concrete slipway at end of Barge House Rd, turning off Woolwich Manor Way/Albert Rd: site is muddy at LW

Woolwich - launch from Bell Water Gate on the south side of the river: access is from Woolwich High St and the ramp is steep and parking difficult.

Gravesend Canal Basin - turn off M 2 following signs to Gravesend East, going along Valley Drive and into Abbey Rd, tuirning left into Milton Rd and right into Ordnance Rd: turn left at Canal Road onto the Promenade and look for the wooden bridge; site is adjacent. Concrete and wooden ramp available at all states of tide and suitable all craft: lock opens from one hour before to HW. Petrol, parking for car and trailer in compound (c), crane, toilets and showers (c), chandlery from Miller Marine or Starbucks. Speed limit 3mph: no water-skiing. Further information from the lock-master Tel Gravesend(0474) 352392/337489. Charge (licence required) and harbour dues payable.

River Trent
The river below Shardlow is controlled by BW with whom boats using this section of the river are required to register. The river gives access to the Trent and Mersey Canal, Erewash Canal and R Soar Navigation. Speed limit 8mph downstream of Long Eaton and 6mph upstream: water-skiing is allowed in some areas: consult P Parr Esq, Treasurer, Trent Powerboat and Ski Club, 6 Nottingham Rd, Bottesford, Notts.

Sawley Bridge Marina (Davidson Boatbuilers) Ltd, Long Eaton
Leave M 1 at junction 24 taking A 6 towards Derby then B 6540 to Sawley. Concrete slipway into 10' water suitable all boats and available daily from 0900-1730 (winter) and 0900-2030 (summer). Fuel, parking for car and trailer (c), toilets, boatyard facilities, cafe and caravan park. Assisted launch and recovery and 10 ton crane available. Further information Tel Long Eaton(0602) 4278. BW licence available here. Charge and licence required.

Shardlow Marina
Leave M 1 at junction 24, taking A 6 towards Derby. Concrete slipway into 10' water available 10 hours a day on weekdays only. No fuel, parking for car and trailer (c), toilets and showers, chandlery, moorings. Further information Tel Derby(0332) 792832. Charge and licence required.

Nottingham Castle Marina, Castle Boulevard

Leave M 1 at junction 25 taking A 52 to city: site is on Beeston Canal. Concrete slipway with gradual gradient into 4/6' water available daily from 0900-1700 Tel Nottingham (0602) 412672. Diesel, parking for car and trailer (c) toilets, chandlery. Speed limit 5 knots in canal. Charge and licence required.

Colwick Park Marina, Nottingham

Leave M 1 at junction 25 taking A 52 to city: site is on east side of town. Concrete slipway available daily from 0900-1730 Tel Nottingham (0602) 608161. Fuel nearby, parking for car and trailer (c), toilets, chandlery. Charge and licence required.

Ferry Boat Inn, Stoke Bardolph

From Nottingham take the A 612 north east following signs to village. Gentle concrete slipway into approx 5'water available 0900-2100 daily and suitable all craft. Fuel, parking for car (c), toilets, telephone. Speed limit 4mph. Charge and licence required.

Star and Garter Public House, Hazelford Ferry

From A 46 east of Nottingham turn onto the A 6097 then right onto the A 612 to Thurgarton; turn right at the Coach and Horses and follow signs to Bleasby and Star and Garter. Concrete slipway into min 2'water available at all times and suitable all craft. Fuel (3 miles), parking for car and trailer (c) toilets, telephone and pub facilities. Water-skiing for members of TPSC only (see above): no jet skies. No Charge but licence required.

Farndon Harbour Moorings Ltd, North End

Follow A 46 south from Newark turning into Farndon main street then right into Marsh Lane, left into The Nurseries and right into the harbour. Concrete slipway available 24 hours a day Tel Newark(0636) 705483. Diesel on site, petrol (1 mile), parking for car and trailer (c), toilets and showers, chandlery, crane (15 tons) and boat hoist, boatyard facilities. Charge and licence required.

West Stockwith Yacht Basin (Milethorne Marine)

Leave M 18 at junction 1 taking A 631 east to Gainsborough and turning off onto A 161 then after 3 miles turning right after Misterton. Concrete slipway into 9' water available 0800-1700 daily. Fuel, parking for car and trailer (c), toilets, chandlery. Speed limit 4mph. Further information Tel Gainsborough(0427) 890450. Charge and licence required.

West Stockwith BW Yard

Turn off A 631 west of Gainsborough onto A 161 turning right to W Stockwith after passing through Misterton. Concrete slipway into min 3½' water available at all times and suitable all sizes of powered craft. Fuel, parking for car and trailer (c), toilets, telephone, chandlery and yard facilities from W Stockwith Yacht Basin nearby. Charge and licence required.

River Tyne
A busy commercial river. All boats are subject to a minimum conservancy charge by the Port of Tyne Authority. There is a speed limit of 6mph on the river and all waterborne activities are subject to the Authority's byelaws.

Walker Riverside Park, Newcastle

Take A 186 Walker road to Walker Pottery Bank and Riverside Park: access is via a steep, winding road from Pottery Bank car park. Fairly steep concrete slipway available during daylight hours for approx 2 hours either side HW and suitable dinghies and trailer-sailers. Fuel (1 mile), parking for car and trailer (not overnight), toilets and telephone. Check for availability Tel(091) 265 5116. No Charge but licence required.

Gateshead (River Tyne)
Friar's Goose Water Sports Club, Green Lane, Felling
Follow A 6127 from A 1(M) into Gateshead: site is on south side of river. Concrete slipway available for 2/3 hours either side HW. Fuel from local garage, parking for car and trailer, toilets at clubhouse, moorings. Further information Tel Tyneside(091) 4692545. Charge and harbour dues payable.

Derwenthaugh Marina (River Tyne)
Follow signs from the A 69: site is on south bank of river at the confluence of the Rivers Tyne and Derwent near Blaydon and the Scotswood Bridge. Concrete slipway available for 5 hours either side HW and suitable craft up to 35'LOA approx. Fuel, parking for car and trailer, toilets, telephone and chandlers nearby. Speed limit 6mph: fast water zone $\frac{1}{4}$ mile downstream. Site is administered by the Water Sports Assoc: all craft launching here must have 3rd party insurance. Charge and harbour dues payable.

Tyne Riverside Country Park, Newburn
Take A 6085 Newcastle to Newburn road, turning off in Newburn into Grange Rd and following signs. Fairly steep concrete slipway available for approx 2 hours either side HW and suitable small craft only. Fuel ($\frac{1}{2}$ mile), parking for car and trailer (not overnight), toilets and telephone. Site is available to members of the Newburn Waterski Club or to owners of small craft by prior arrangement with the Newburn Riverside Recreation Assoc, Grange Rd, Newburn, Newcastle NE15. Charge and harbour dues payable.

River Wey (Wey and Godalming Navigation)
The river joins the Thames below Shepperton Lock and is owned by the National Trust* from whom a licence should be obtained. Speed limit 4 knots: engine size is restricted to 1 HP per foot length up to a max size of 20HP.

Stoke Lock, Guildford
Leave Guildford on the A 320, turning right into Moorfield Rd and Slyfield Ind Est: after British Telecom building on right, turn down narrow lane marked "private road". Concrete slipway into min 3'water available by prior arrangement only Tel Guildford (0483) 504939 and suitable all craft up to 25'LOA. Fuel, parking for car and trailer (c), toilets and telephone. Charge.

Pyrford Marina, Lock Lane, Pyrford
Turn off A 3 following signs to Wisley Gardens: go through village, past Anchor pub and over canal into Lock Lane: access by this route is limited by a narrow bridge over the canal but an alternative approach can be made from the west. Concrete slipway into min 3'water available by prior arrangement Tel Byfleet(09323) 40739 and suitable craft up to 25/30'LOA. Fuel, parking for car and trailer (c), toilets and telephone. Charge.

River Witham (Witham and Fossdyke Navigation)

Brayford Pool, Lincoln
Situated in the centre of the city and accessible from all main roads. Steep concrete slipway into min 2/3' water available during daylight hours and suitable craft up to 18'LOA. Fuel, parking for car but not for trailer, toilets, chandlers. Speed limit 3mph. No Charge.

Lincoln Marina (James Kendall & Co), Brayford Pool
Situated in the centre of the city and easily accessible. Concrete slipway available from 0900-1700. Diesel, parking for car and trailer (c), toilets, chandlery. Further information Tel Lincoln(0522) 26896. Charge.

Shortferry Marina, Ferry Rd, Fiskerton
Situated between Fiskerton and Bardney. Concrete slipway into 6' water available 0900-2000 daily. Fuel, parking for car and trailer, toilets. Speed limit. Further information Tel Bardney(0526) 398021. Charge.

Belle Isle Marina, The Old Mill, Dogdyke
From A 153 north of Sleaford take Dogdyke Rd from centre of Coningsby for 2 miles: marina is adjacent the Packet Inn. Steep concrete slipway into 4' water suitable craft up to 22'LOA and available 0900-1800 daily. Fuel, parking for car and trailer, crane, winch, toilets, boatyard facilities. Further information Tel Coningsby(0526) 42124. Charge.

NORFOLK BROADS

This area comes under the control of the Broads Authority* and a licence is needed before launching on these waters. Speed limits, generally of 3, 5 or 7mph are enforced and stretches of river are well marked accordingly. Water-skiing is permitted in certain areas at specified times: for further details a copy of the byelaws should be obtained.

Acle (River Bure)
Alan Johnson Boats
From Acle, turn right over river on A 1064. Concrete slipway available 0900-1700 but not fri pm or sat and suitable all craft up to 30'LOA and 10½' wide. Diesel, limited parking for car and trailer (c), toilets and some chandlery. Check for availability Tel Gt Yarmouth(0493) 750481. Charge and licence required.

Barton Turf (Barton Broad)
The Staithe, Cox Bros Boatyard
Follow A 1151 from Norwich. Concrete slipway for craft up to 20'LOA available 0800-1800 daily Easter to Sept by prior arrangement. No fuel, limited parking for car and trailer (c), toilets. Further information Tel Smallburgh(069 260) 206. Charge and licence required.

Beccles (River Waveney)
Beccles Yacht Station
From A 146 Beccles bypass follow signs to the Quay. Concrete slipway available for 3 hours either side HW and suitable craft up to 20'LOA. Fuel, parking for car and trailer (c), toilets, crane, chandlery from Jeckells. Further information Tel Beccles(0502) 712225. No Charge but licence required.

Beccles (River Waveney)
Aston Boats, Bridge Wharf
Leave Beccles on the Old Norwich road: site is on right 200yds after bridge and opposite Beccles Yacht Station. Concrete slipway available for approx 4 hours either side HW 0800-1800 but not fri or sat and suitable all craft. Diesel, parking for car and trailer (c), toilets. Check for availability Tel Beccles(0502) 713960. Charge and licence required.

Beccles (River Waveney)
Waveney Valley Boats, Puddingmoor
Follow A 146 from Norwich or Lowestoft. Steel slipway available during working hours only at all states of tide: 3' water at end at LW. Fuel nearby, parking for car and trailer (c), toilets, crane and all boatyard facilities. By prior arrangement only Tel Beccles(0502) 712538. Charge and licence required.

Brundall (River Yare)
Brundall Marina, Riverside Estate
Follow A 47 from Norwich: access is over level crossing at Brundall Station. Concrete slipway available during working hours and at all states of tide for craft up to 18'LOA. Fuel nearby, parking for car and trailer (c), toilets, chandlers nearby. Further information Tel Norwich(0603) 715029. Charge and licence required.

Burgh Castle (River Waveney)
Burgh Castle Marina
From Great Yarmouth follow A 12 south and minor roads. Concrete slipway available from 0900-1300 and 1400-1800 (1700 in winter) daily for 4/5 hours either side HW. Diesel, parking for car and trailer, toilets, chandlery, pub. Further information Tel Gt Yarmouth(0493) 780331. Charge (min period one week with parking) and licence required.

Burgh St Peter (River Waveney)
Waveney River Centre
Follow A 143 from Beccles and minor roads. Concrete slipway available at all states of tide. Fuel, parking for car and trailer (c), toilets. Further information Tel Aldeby(0502) 77217. Charge and licence required.

Hickling (Hickling Broad)
Whispering Reeds Boatyard
Follow A 149 from Gt Yarmouth. Concrete slipway available at all times for boats with up to 2' draught. Diesel, parking for car and trailer (c), toilets. Further information Tel Hickling (069 261) 314. Charge and licence required.

Hickling (Hickling Broad)
Pleasure Boat Inn
Follow A 149 from Gt Yarmouth: site is adjacent Pleasure Boat Inn. Concrete slipway available at all times for launching dinghies only. No fuel, parking for car and trailer (c), toilets. Further information Tel Hickling (069 261) 211. Charge and licence required.

Horning (River Bure)
The Street
Follow A 1062 Wroxham to Potter Heigham road. Concrete slipway near Swan Inn available at all times. Fuel in village, limited parking for car and trailer, toilets nearby, obtain key from the Swan Inn. Charge and licence required.

Horning (River Bure)
Percival Boats Ltd, Ferry Corner
Follow the A 1062 Wroxham to Potter Heigham road turning right at sign to Horning village. Two concrete and wood slipways available at all times. Fuel, parking for car and trailer (c), toilets, chandlery. Further information Tel Horning(0692) 630461. Charge and licence required.

Horning (River Bure)
Horning Pleasurecraft Ltd
Follow A 1062 from Wroxham turning right to Horning village then turn down gravel lane on right after passing Percival Boats and yard is on left. Launching by hoist available 0900-1800 daily suitable craft up to 6 tons weight on trailer and with 3' draught. Fuel, parking for car and trailer (c), toilets, boatyard facilities on site. Further information Tel Horning (0692) 630366. Charge and licence required.

Loddon (River Chet)
Worsley Craft Ltd
Turn off A 146 towards Loddon: yard is down track opposite service station. Boat lift available for 5 hours either side HW during working hours or at other times by prior arrangement and suitable craft up to 35'LOA, 10½' wide and 8 tons: max height of boat on trailer 10½'. Diesel, parking for car and trailer (c). Check for availability Tel Loddon(0508) 20397. Charge and licence required.

Ludham Bridge (River Ant)
Ludham Bridge Services, Johnson St
Follow A 1062 Wroxham to Potter Heigham road. Hand gantry up to 14' and mobile crane (6 tons) available from 0900-1700 daily. Fuel, parking for car and trailer (c), chandlery and boatyard facilities, toilets. Further information Tel Horning(0692) 630486. Charge and licence required.

Martham (River Thurne)
Martham Boat Building Co, Riverside, Cess Road
Follow A 149 from Gt Yarmouth. Concrete slipway available at all times during working hours but not sat am. Fuel, parking for car and trailer (c), toilets. Contact Gt Yarmouth (0493) 740249. Charge and licence required.

Oulton Broad
Oulton Broad Yacht Station
Follow A 146 Beccles to Lowestoft road: site is just south of the road bridge. Concrete slipway available for 3 hours either side HW suitable craft up to 30'LOA. Fuel, parking for car and trailer, crane, toilets, chandlery from Jeckells opposite. Further information from the Harbour Master Tel Lowestoft(0502) 574946. No Charge but licence required.

Oulton Broad
Water Sports Centre (North Bay)
Follow A 146 Beccles to Lowestoft road crossing over the bridge to the north shore. Concrete slipway available at Water Sports Centre and suitable all craft. Further information from The Harbour Master Tel Lowestoft(0502) 574946. No Charge but licence required.

Oulton Broad
Wherry Hotel
Follow A 146 Beccles to Lowestoft road. Concrete slipway available at all times. Fuel, parking for car and trailer (c), toilets, chandlery from Jeckells. Apply hotel Tel Lowestoft(0502) 3521. Charge and licence required.

Oulton Broad
Colman's Land Slipway, Bridge Road
Follow A 146 Beccles to Lowestoft road. Concrete slipway available at all times. Fuel nearby, parking for car and trailer (c) nearby, toilets, chandlers. No Charge but licence required. .

Ranworth Broad (off River Bure)
Ranworth Maltings Yard
Take B 1140 from Norwich to Panxworth then follow signs to Ranworth. Concrete slipway into min 3'water available during daylight hours and suitable all craft up to 30'LOA and 10 tons max. No fuel, parking for car and trailer, toilets, telephone: chandlery and yard facilities available from Ludham Bridge Services. Further information Tel Horning(0692) 630486. Charge and licence required.

Reedham Ferry (River Yare)
Reedham Ferry Inn
Follow B 1140 north from Beccles or B 1140 south from Acle. Concrete slipway available from 0800-2200 suitable craft up to 35'LOA. No fuel, parking for car and trailer, toilets. Keep clear of chain ferry and beware deceptive tidal flow here. Apply to Mr Archer at the Inn Tel Gt Yarmouth (0493) 700429. Charge and licence required.

Repps (Repps Staithe)
Follow A 149 north from Gt Yarmouth. Concrete slipway available at all times for craft up to 16'LOA. No fuel, limited parking for car and trailer (c). No Charge but licence required.

St Olaves (River Waveney)
Follow A 143 Beccles to Gt Yarmouth road: site is by bridge and opposite the Bell Inn. Concrete slipway available at all times and suitable small craft only. Fuel, parking for car and trailer nearby. Obtain key from Bridge Stores Tel(0493) 488230. Charge and licence required.

Stalham (River Ant)
Richardsons (New Horizon) Ltd.
Follow A 149 north from Gt Yarmouth. Concrete slipway available mon-sat and sun morning in season. Diesel, parking for car and trailer (c), crane, toilets. Further information Tel Stalham(0692) 81081. Charge and licence required.

Stalham (River Ant)
Stalham Yacht Services
Follow A 149 north from Gt Yarmouth. Concrete slipway available mon-fri and sun. Fuel, parking for car and trailer (c), toilets. Further information Tel Stalham(0692) 80288. Charge and licence required.

Thorpe (River Yare)
Griffin Marine
Turn off A 47 Gt Yarmouth to Norwich Rd at Thorpe. Concrete slipway into 4' water available at all times and suitable craft up to 12' wide. Fuel, parking for car and trailer (c), crane, toilets and boatyard facilities. Further information Tel Norwich(0603) 33253. Charge and licence required.

CANAL SITES

Most canals are controlled by British Waterways (BW)* who require pleasure boats using the canals to obtain a licence before entering the water. Licences are issued in advance by the Craft Licensing Office* and cover all the navigable waterways under the Board's control. There is a general speed limit on the canals of 4mph and movement of boats after dusk is prohibited.

Basingstoke Canal
The canal is currently being restored and at present is separated from the Wey Navigation by 6 miles of dewatered canal: it is hoped that restoration work will be completed by late 1990/1991. Before launching into the canal a licence should be obtained: short-term licences can be obtained by post or telephone from the Canal Office, Ash Lock Cottage, Government Rd, Aldershot GU11 2PS Tel Farnborough(0252) 513385. There is a speed limit of 4mph on the canal.

Aldershot, Farnborough Road
In Aldershot, leave A 325 at junction with A 323 just south of canal: access is via one-way system on west side dual carriageway and may be difficult during biennial Army/Air Show. Concrete slipway into min 3'water available during daylight hours. No fuel, parking for car and trailer. No Charge but licence required.

Potters Pub Slipway, Mytchett Place Road, Mytchett
Follow A 321 north from Farnborough and signs to Mytchett: site is north of Mytchett Lake on the east side of the canal and adjacent Potters Steakhouse. Concrete slipway into 2' water available during daylight hours and suitable small craft. No fuel, parking for car and trailer, toilets at Potters Steakhouse nearest chandlers Surrey and Hants Marine, Ash Wharf, Aldershot. No Charge but licence required.

Barley Mow Pub, Winchfield
From Aldershot follow A 325 west to Fleet turning off to follow signs: site is at Barley Mow Bridge on east side of road and opposite Barley Mow Pub. Concrete slipway into 2' water available during daylight hours and suitable small craft. No fuel, parking for car and trailer, toilets at pub, nearest chandlers Surrey and Hants Marine, Ash Wharf, Aldershot. No Charge but licence required.

Birmingham Canal
The first canal was built from Aldersley on the Staffordshire and Worcestershire Canal to Birmingham and the network which subsequently developed was the result of three rival companies each trying to monopolise the traffic. Over one hundred miles of the network are still navigable. BW licence required.

M E Braine (Boatbuilders) Ltd, Norton Canes
Leave M 6 at junction 12 following A 5 east: site is between Cannock and Brownhills. Launching available at all times. Fuel, parking for car and trailer, toilets, cranage by arrangement. Further information Tel Brownhills(054 33) 4888. Charge and licence required.

Bridgewater Canal
Built to transport coal from the Duke of Bridgewater's mines at Worsley to Manchester, the canal was later extended to join the Trent & Mersey Canal at Preston Brook and the Leeds and Liverpool Canal at Leigh. All craft using the canal must be licenced with the Estates Office, Manchester Ship Canal Co, boats holding a BW licence may cruise the canal for up to seven days.

Lymm Marina

Leave M 6 at junction 20 taking B 5158. Concrete slipway available during normal business hours or at other times by arrangement Tel Lymm(092 575) 2945. Diesel, parking for car and trailer (c), toilets, chandlers. Site suitable for small centreboard craft only. Charge and licence required.

Calder and Hebble Navigation
Built to improve and extend navigation on the Calder above Wakefield to Sowerby Bridge, the canal connected with the Huddersfield Broad and Narrow Canals and the Rochdale Canal.

Sowerby Marine, The Wharf

Follow A 58 east from Rochdale to Sowerby Bridge. Concrete slipway available daily from 0830-1730 Tel Halifax(0422) 32922. Fuel, parking for car and trailer, toilets and showers, chandlery. Charge and licence required.

Elland Wharf, Elland

From Bradford follow A 641 south and A 6025 through Elland, turning off into Gas Works Lane (off Elland Bridge) and onto Elland Wharf. Slipway into 5' water available 0800-2000 daily. Fuel, parking for car but not for trailer. Get permission to launch and key from Mr Dix, 41 Victoria Wharf or Mr W Carey (Junior), Wharf House. Charge and licence required.

Saville Town Wharf (Robinsons Hire Cruisers Ltd), Dewsbury

From Leeds follow A 62 south, turning into Mill Street East in Dewsbury. Concrete and steel slipway into 4' water available during normal working hours and at weekends suitable all craft up to 57½'LOA and 4' draught. Fuel, parking for car and trailer (c), crane and winch available for hire, toilets, boatyard facilities on site. Further information Tel Dewsbury(0924) 467976. Charge and licence required.

Caledonian Canal

Caley Marina, Canal Road, Inverness

From the A 9 take A 82 through Inverness crossing the river at Kenneth St traffic lights and turning right to Beauly on A 862: after 1 mile cross Muirtown Bridge and turn sharp left up Canal Road; at lock top bear left along canal-side towpath. Slipway available 0900-1800 (mon-sat). Fuel, parking for car and trailer (c), toilets, chandlery and boatyard facilities on site. Further information Tel Inverness(0463) 236539. Speed limit 6mph on canal but no speed limit on lochs. Charge.

Great Glen Water Park, South Laggan By Spean Bridge

From Fort William follow A 82 towards Inverness as far as Loch Oich: just before South Laggan swing bridge turn right and follow signs to Water Park. Steep concrete slipway into min 2' water available 0900-2000 daily suitable boats up to 20'LOA. Diesel, parking for car and trailer, toilets, shop, bar and restaurant. Speed limit on canal 6 mph. Further information Tel Invergarry(08093) 223. No Charge but permission to launch required.

Chelmer and Blackwater Navigation

Paper Mill Lock, Little Baddow

From Chelmsford follow A 414 towards Maldon turning off at Danbury. Launching by prior arrangement only from concrete slipway. Fuel (3 miles), parking for car and trailer (c), chandlers at Heybridge Basin. Further information from Chelmer and Blackwater Navigation Co, Tel Danbury(024 541) 5520. Speed limit 4mph. Charge and licence required.

Chesterfield Canal

The canal was originally built to facilitate the transport of goods from the Chesterfield area to the sea via the River Trent and ran from Chesterfield to West Stockwith where it joined the river. The navigable section now runs from Worksop to West Stockwith: the river lock is manned Tel Gainsborough(0427) 890204 and is normally accessible from 2½ hours before to 4 hours after HW.

West Stockwith Yacht Basin (Milethorne Marine)

Leave M 18 at junction 1 taking A 631 east to Gainsborough and turning off onto A 161 then after 3 miles turning right after Misterton. Concrete slipway into 9' water available 0800-1700 daily. Fuel, parking for car and trailer (c), toilets, chandlery. Further information Tel Gainsborough(0427) 890450. Charge and licence required.

West Stockwith BW Yard

Turn off A 631 west of Gainsborough onto A 161 turning right to W Stockwith after passing through Misterton. Concrete slipway into min 3½'water available at all times and suitable all sizes of powered craft. Fuel, parking for car and trailer (c), toilets, telephone, chandlery and yard facilities from W Stockwith Yacht Basin nearby. Charge and licence required.

Drakeshole Tunnel

Turn off the A 631 Gainsborough to Bawtry road. Wooden ramp into min 3' water available during daylight hours and suitable all powered craft. No fuel, parking for car and trailer, pub. No Charge but licence required.

Retford (Retford Mariners Boat Club)

Turn left off A 638 London Road at lights, going down Albert Rd, opposite Albert Pub. Concrete slipway into min 3'water available during daylight hours and suitable all powered craft. Fuel, parking for car and trailer, toilets, chandlery from Ultra Marine, Bridgegate. Charge and licence required.

Coventry Canal

Built to connect Coventry with the Trent and Mersey Canal and to provide cheap coal from Bedworth coalfield this was one of the most prosperous canals.

Swan Lane Wharf, Stoke Heath, Coventry (Club Line Cruisers)

Leave M 6 at junction 2 taking A 46 towards City centre: after passing under railway bridge turn first right into Swan Lane. Fairly steep slipway with min 2' water suitable craft up to 20'LOA available 0900-1700 (mon-fri). Petrol, parking for car and trailer (c), toilets, boatyard facilities on site. Further information Tel Coventry(0203) 58864. Charge and licence required.

Forth & Clyde Canal

The canal is obstructed by road crossings but reasonable lengths are available for cruising. For further information contact the Forth and Clyde Countryside Ranger*. There is a speed limit of 6mph and a BW licence is required.

Townhead, Kirkintilloch to Maryhill (6½ miles): height restriction 6'.

Hay's Slip, Southbank Road, Kirkintilloch

Follow A 803 from Glasgow turning into Southbank Road. Large slip with good surface available during daylight hours and suitable most craft. Fuel nearby, parking for car and trailer. No Charge but licence required.

Stables Inn, Glasgow Road Bridge
Follow the A 803 1½ miles west of Kirkintilloch. Large concrete slipway with rails and boat trolley and smaller wooden ramp. Fuel, parking for car and trailer. Slip is operated by Canalside Leisure Ltd Tel 0836- 704287 for availability. Charge and licence required.

Sandbank Street, Maryhill
Follow A 81 from Glasgow. Fairly steep timber and concrete slipway suitable small craft up to 13'LOA available during daylight hours. No Charge but licence required.

Ruchill St Bridge to Old Basin Hamiltonhill (1 mile but includes Firhill Basin)

Firhill Basin
Access is via Firhill Rd and site is adjacent to road bridge. Stone slipway available during daylight hours and suitable craft up to 13'LOA. Parking for car and trailer. Contact Canal Foreman Tel Glasgow (041) 332 1065 for key. No charge but licence required.

Old Basin Works, Hamiltonhill
A large slipway with a rough surface suitable for launching by 4- wheel drive vehicles only. Contact Canal Foreman Tel Glasgow(041) 332 1065 to arrange access. No Charge but licence required.

Auchinstarry to Wyndford (4 miles)

Auchinstarry
Follow A 803 towards Kilsyth turning onto B 802: site is located next to BW depot and access road is immediately adjacent to bridge on south east side of canal. Slipway with hardcore surface suitable boats up to 25'LOA. No fuel, parking for car and trailer. No Charge but licence required.

Grand Union Canal
Comprising eight separate canals, the Grand Union connects London with Birmingham, Leicester and Nottingham. BW licence required.

Brentford Yacht and Boat Co Ltd, Brentford
Follow A 4 west from Chiswick: access is via Brent Way and site is close junction of canal and River Thames. Concrete slipway available from 0800-1800 daily for 1 hour either side HW and suitable craft up to 20'LOA. No fuel, parking for car and trailer (c), toilets. Charge and licence required.

High Line Yachting, Iver (Slough Arm)
Leave M 4 at junction 5 taking B 470 to Iver: access is via Mansion Lane. Very steep concrete slipway with drop at end available from 0900-1330/1430-1800 (mon-sat) and 1100-1700 (sun) and suitable small craft only Tel Iver(0753) 651496. Diesel, parking for car and trailer (c), toilets, chandlery. Charge and licence required.

Uxbridge Boat Centre, Uxbridge Wharf
Leave M 4 at junction 4 following A 408 north and turning onto A 4007: access is via narrow and congested residential streets. Concrete slipway into min 4' water available 0900-1800 (tues-sat), 1100-1600 (sun). Fuel, limited parking for car and trailer, crane and winch available from yard staff, toilets, chandlery and boatyard facilities on site. By prior arrangement only Tel Uxbridge(0895) 52019. Charge and licence required.

Denham Marina, 100 Acres
Leave M 40 at junction 1 taking A 412 north. Concrete slipway available 0900-1700 (mon-sat) and 0900-1200 (sun) Tel Uxbridge(0895) 39811. Fuel, parking for car and trailer, chandlery. Charge and licence required.

Harefield Marina, Moorhall Road, Harefield
Turn off A 40 onto A 412, turning off into Moorhall Rd. Launching over shingle hard into min 3' water available 0900-1730 daily and suitable all craft. Diesel, parking for car and trailer, crane, chandlery. Further information Tel Harefield(089582) 2036. Charge and licence required.

Cassio Bridge Marina, Watford
Follow M 1 turning off at junction 6. Concrete slipway available from 0900-1730 daily
Tel Watford(0923) 34113. No fuel, parking for car and trailer, toilets and showers,
chandlery. Charge and licence required.

Willowbridge Enterprises, Stoke Road, Bletchley
Leave M 1 at junction 9 taking A 5 to Bletchley: site is on A 4146. Concrete slipway
available during business hours or at other times by arrangement Tel Milton
Keynes(0908) 643242. Fuel, parking for car and trailer (c), toilets and showers,
chandlery and all yard facilities. Site suitable for trailed craft up to 30'LOA: crane
available. Charge and licence required.

Baxter Boatfitting Services, The Wharf, Yardley Gobion
Follow signs from the A 508 south of Northampton, site is at Bridge 60: access limits
length of craft which can be launched here. Concrete slipway into min 3'water suitable
craft up to 7' wide and 30'LOA. Check for availability Tel Yardley Gobion(0908)
542844. Charge and licence required.

Stoke Locks, Stoke Bruerne
Leave M 1 at junction 15 taking A 508 south: site is where road crosses canal. Concrete
slipway available at all times. Fuel from Yardley Wharf or Stoke Bruerne Wharf, parking
for car and trailer in public car park, toilets in village, chandlers and crane at Yardley
Wharf. No Charge but licence required.

Gayton Yard, Blisworth
Turn off A 43 south of Northampton following signs to Gayton: further directions can be
obtained from yard by sending a sae. Concrete slipway into min 4'water available at all
times and suitable craft up to 30'LOA. Fuel, no parking, telephone, chandlers and
boatyards nearby. Speed limit 4mph. Further information Tel Blisworth(0604) 858233.
No Charge but licence required.

Whilton Marina, Whilton Locks, Daventry
Leave M 1 at junction 16 following A 45 and A 5 north: site is 3 miles north of Weedon.
Concrete slipway into min 3½'water available from 0900-1300/1400-1800 Tel
Daventry(0327) 842577 suitable all craft. Fuel, parking for car and trailer (c), toilets and
showers, chandlery. Charge and licence required.

Braunston Marina (Ladyline Ltd)
Leave M 1 at junction 16 taking A 45: site is 3 miles west of Daventry. Slipway of
concrete and wood available from 0900-1900 (mon-sat) 1000-1900 (sun) Tel
Rugby(0788) 890325. Fuel and gas, parking for car and trailer (c), toilets and showers,
chandlery. Charge and licence required.

Calcutt Boats Ltd, Stockton, Nr Rugby
Turn off A 425 to Stockton between Daventry and Southam. Concrete slipway into
Warwick and Napton Section of canal with min 6½' water avaialable 0900-1730 daily
and suitable craft up to 6' 10'' wide. Diesel, calor gas, parking for car and trailer, toilets,
chandlery on site. Further information Tel Southam(092 681) 3757. Charge and licence
required.

Kilworth Marina (Hucker Marine Ltd), North Kilworth (Leicester Section)
Turn off M 1 at junction 20 taking A 427 east: site is between N Kilworth and Husbands
Bosworth. Concrete slipway available 0900-1800 daily suitable craft up to 30'LOA and
6' 10'' wide. Fuel, parking for car and trailer (c), toilets, chandlery and boatyard
facilities on site. Further information Tel Market Harborough(0858) 880484. Charge and
licence required.

Foxton Boat Services, Bottom Lock, Foxton (Leicester Section)
Leave M 1 at junction 20 taking A 427 to Market Harborough and following signs to
Foxton Locks. Concrete slipway into min 2' water available at all times by prior
arrangement only and suitable craft up to 70'LOA and 14' wide. Fuel, parking for car
and trailer (c), crane, toilets and showers, chandlery and boatyard facilities on site.
Further information Tel Kibworth(083 753) 2285. Charge and licence required.

Leicester Marina, Old Bridge, Thurcaston Road (Soar Navigation)
From Leicester follow outer ring road. Steep concrete slipway (1:5) into min 4' water
available during normal working hours. Fuel, parking for car and trailer (c), crane, winch,
toilets, chandlery and boatyard facilities on site. Speed limit on R Soar is 6mph. Further
information Tel Leicester(0533) 662194. Charge and licence required.

Old Junction Boatyard (L R Harris & Son), Syston (Soar Navigation)
Follow A 46 and A 607 out of Leicester. Concrete slipway into min 4½' water available
0900-2100 (summer) and 0900-1800 (winter). Fuel, parking for car and trailer (c), toilets,
chandlery and boatyard facilities on site. Further information Tel Leicester(0533) 692135.
Charge and licence facilities.

Sileby Mill Boatyard, Mountsorrel Lane (Soar Navigation)
Follow A 6 north from Leicester turning onto B 674 at Mountsorrel and following signs:
pass through entrance gate with care. Concrete slipway (1:9) into min 3½'water available
during daylight hours (not mon) and suitable powered craft. Petrol, diesel on site,
parking for car and trailer, toilets, telephone, limited chandlery and yard facilities on
site. Further information Tel Sileby(050 981) 3583. Charge and licence required.

Grantham Canal

Denton Wharf
From A 1 take A 607 towards Melton Mowbray turning right into Denton Village and
right again in the village to get to the wharf: this site gives acces to three miles of canal.
Fairly steep concrete slipways available during daylight hours and suitable dinghies. No
fuel, parking for car and trailer. No Charge.

Huddersfield Broad Canal
**It is advisable to inform the lock-keeper if you wish to navigate the canal Tel
Huddersfield(0484) 36732. BW licence required.**

Aspley Basin (Aspley Wharf Marina Ltd)
Turn off M 62 at junction 23: site is on A 629, Wakefield Rd. Concrete slipway with min
depth 4' available during normal business hours. Fuel, parking for car and trailer (c),
toilets, chandlery and boatyard facilities on site. Further information Tel Huddersfield
(0484) 514123. Charge and licence required.

Huddersfield Narrow Canal
**Restoration work is still in progress on this canal and navigable sections do
not at present connect. For further information contact the Huddersfield Canal
Society*. For further details of launching facilities on the Kirklees Section
contact Mr Ian Preston c/o Kirklees Council, Linthwaite Workshops,
Huddersfield.**

Huddersfield Polytechnic, Wakefield Road
Site is adjacent A 629. Concrete slipway into min 3' water available during daylight
hours suitable craft up to 20'LOA. Fuel, parking for car and trailer (c), toilets, chandlery
from Aspley Marina. Contact T Gaskell, Pro Rector, Huddersfield Polytechnic,
Queensgate, Huddersfield before launching. Charge.

Kennet & Avon Canal

By mid-summer 1990 the Kennet and Avon Canal will finally be cleared of all obstructions to navigation from Reading to Bristol. Use of the Crofton and Devizes flights of locks may be restricted due to limitations in the water supply. Further information from BW Devizes Tel Devizes(0380) 722859.

Tyle Mill Lock, Sulhamstead

Follow A 4 west from Reading turning off south to Sulhamstead by Three Kings Jacks Booth pub. Launching is possible by the lock for small craft which can be manhandled only: access is by BW key. Further information from BW Padworth Depot*. No Charge but licence required.

Greenham Island, Mill Lane, Newbury

Leave M 4 at junction 13 taking the A 34 south and turning left at the second roundabout into Mill Lane: take first right by Greenham Mill housing complex and head for the canal bank and gateway on left. Concrete and wood slipway into 6' water available 0900-1700 or at other times by arrangement and suitable craft up to 25'LOA and 2'draught. Petrol nearby, diesel on site, parking for car and trailer (c), winch, toilets, crane and yard facilities from Newbury Boat Co on site. Please Tel Newbury(0635) 42884 to arrange use of slipway. Charge and licence required.

Oakhill Down, Little Bedwyn

Turn off A 4 at Hungerford onto A 338 and follow signs. Steep slipway of steel shuttering and concrete available at all times and suitable craft up to 23'LOA and 3' draught. Further information from BW Padworth Depot*. No Charge but licence required.

Pewsey Wharf

Turn off A 4 at Marlborough following A 345 south: site is $\frac{1}{2}$ mile north of Pewsey village. Steel slipway into min $3\frac{1}{2}$' water available during daylight hours and suitable craft up to 23'LOA and $1\frac{1}{2}$' draught and max weight 3 tons (boat and trailer). No fuel, parking for car, leave trailer by arrangement with Warden, toilets, pub nearby. The canal is shallow here and it is not recommended that boats with a draught of more than $1\frac{1}{2}$' should attempt to navigate. No Charge but licence required.

Devizes Wharf

Follow A 342 north from Andover. Steep concrete slipway available during daylight hours and suitable craft up to 23'LOA and 3' draught. Fuel nearby, parking for car and trailer, toilets. No Charge but licence required.

Tranquil Boats, Lock House, Semington

Follow A 350 north from A 361 east of Trowbridge, turning right before bridge over canal. Concrete slipway available during daylight hours. Fuel from nearby garage, parking for car and trailer, tractor assistance available. Further information Tel(0380) 870654. Charge and licence required.

Hilperton Marina, Hammond Way (Kennet & Avon Nav Co Ltd)

From Trowbridge follow A 361 east and B 3105 towards Staverton: access is through Trowbridge Canal Industrial Estate. Fairly steep concrete slipway available by prior arrangement only into min 4' water suitable craft up to 23'LOA, 10' wide and with 3' draught. Fuel, parking for car (c), leave trailer by arrangement (c), crane by arrangement, toilets, chandlers on site. Further information Tel Trowbridge(0225) 65243. Charge and licence required.

Bradford-on-Avon Wharf, Frome Road

Follow A 3109 south from Bradford-on-Avon: site is at lock 14. Steep concrete slipway with hand winch and drop at end into 4' water available 0800- dusk and suitable craft up to 23'LOA with 3' draught. Fuel, parking for car but not for trailer, toilets, canal shop, pump out. Charge and licence required.

Bradford-on-Avon Marina
Turn off the main Bradford-on-Avon to Trowbridge road (A 363). Steep concrete slipway available during daylight hours and suitable craft up to 70'LOA and 12' wide. Fuel, parking for car and trailer, toilets and showers for boat owners only, chandlery from Widbrook Chandlery on site, restaurant. Further information Tel Bradford-on-Avon(02216) 4562. Charge and licence required.

Lancaster Canal

The Jolly Roger (Adventure Cruisers), Catforth
Leave M 55 at junction 1 taking A 6 north, then B 5269 and minor roads west: access restricts size of craft to 24'LOA. Steep concrete slipway available 0800-2000 into 4' water. Fuel, parking for car and trailer (c), toilets, chandlery and boatyard facilities on site. By prior arrangement only, especially at weekends Tel Preston(0772) 690232. Charge.

Marina Park, Galgate
Leave M 6 at junction 3: site is on A 6 heading towards Lancaster, on Glasgow Arm of canal giving access to the sea. Concrete slipway into min 5' water available at all times and suitable craft up to 60'LOA except keeled yachts. Fuel, parking for car and trailer (c), crane, winch, toilets, chandlery and boatyard facilities on site. Further information Tel Lancaster (0524) 751 368.

Leeds & Liverpool Canal
The longest canal built by one company, the Leeds and Liverpool Canal connects Leeds to the River Mersey at Liverpool via the Stanley Dock Branch and to the River Douglas and thence the Ribble estuary at Tarleton via the Rufford Branch. In Leeds, the canal connects with the Aire and Calder Navigations at River Lock.

James Mayor & Co Ltd, Tarleton (Rufford Branch)
Leave M 6 at junction 31 following A 59 west until just before junction with A 565: go through Tarleton village and down Plox Brow to canal bank then turn left. Concrete slipway available during normal business hours Tel Hesketh Bank(077473) 2250. Fuel, parking for car and trailer (c), toilets, chandlery. Site gives access to sea via River Douglas for 2½ hours at each HW. Charge and licence required.

White Bear Marina, Park Road, Adlington
Leave M 61 at junction 6 taking A 6 north to Adlington. Concrete slipway available from 0830-2100 (mon-fri) and 1000-2100 (sat & sun) Tel Adlington(0257) 481054. Fuel, parking for car and trailer (c), toilets and showers, chandlery. Charge and licence required.

Silsden Boats, The Wharf, Silsden
Turn off A 629 north of Keighley onto the A 6034: site is approached via Elliott St. Concrete slipway into min 5½'water available 0800-1730 mon- fri and sun and suitable small craft and narrow boats up to 60'LOA. Diesel, parking for car and trailer, yard facilities. Further information Tel Steeton(0535) 53675. Charge and licence required.

Hainsworths Boatyard Ltd, Fairfax Road, Bingley
From Bradford, take A 650 to Bingley turning into Park Rd, Hall Bank Drive and Beck Lane and going straight on at the roundabout: Fairfax Rd is at the very end on the left and the site is just above Five Rise Locks. Concrete slipway into min 3½'water available 0830-2100 during the summer and suitable all craft. Fuel(½ mile), parking for car and trailer (c), telephone and chandlers (½ mile), yard facilities on site. BW licence available on site. Charge and licence required.

Rodley Boat Centre, Canal Wharf, Rodley
Site is off Leeds Outer Ring Road and adjacent A 657. Fairly steep concrete and wood slipway into 6' water available 0900-2000. Fuel, calor gas, oil, parking for car and trailer (c), toilets, chandlery and other facilities on site. Further information Tel Leeds(0532) 576132. Charge and licence required.

Fallwood Marina, Pollard Lane, Leeds
Site is on the Leeds to Bradford road. Concrete slipway into min 4' water available 0900-1730 (mon-fri), 1000-1600 (sat-sun) and closed all day tues. No fuel, parking for car and trailer (c), toilets. Further information Tel Leeds(0532) 581074. Charge and licence required.

Llangollen Canal
Originally planned to connect the Mersey to the Severn, the canal is now navigable from Llantisilio just north of Llangollen (for small craft only) to Hurleston Junction where it connects with the Shropshire Union. With the spectacular aqueducts at Chirk and Poncysyllte, this is probably the most popular cruising canal in the country.

Maestermyn Marine Ltd, Whittington, Oswestry
Turn off the A 5 north-east of Oswestry onto the A 495: site is adjacent to road between Whittington and Ellesmere. Concrete slipway into min 3' water available 0900-1800 (other times by arrangement) and suitable all craft. Diesel on site, petrol($\frac{1}{2}$ mile), parking for car and trailer (c), outboard engine repairs, toilets, telephone and chandlery, pub and restaurant facilities on site. Further information Tel Oswestry(0691) 662424. Charge and licence required.

Black Prince Marina, Alders Lane, Whixall
Follow M 54 and A 5 to Shrewsbury then take A 528 and B 5476 to Wem and local roads to Whixall: site is on former Prees Branch of canal. Concrete slipway available from 0900-1700 daily Tel Whixall(094872) 420/540. Diesel, parking for car and trailer, toilets. Charge.

Macclesfield Canal
The canal was built to connect the Midlands and Manchester and runs from Marple on the Peak Forest Canal to Kidsgrove on the Trent and Mersey Canal: it now forms part of the 100 mile "Cheshire Ring" canal circuit.

Heritage Narrow Boats Ltd, Kent Green
Leave M 6 at junction 16 taking A 500 east then A 34 towards Congleton: 1$\frac{1}{2}$ miles after crossing A 50 turn right into Station Rd (signposted to Mow Cop), turn left after crossing canal and marina is 100 yds on left: site is 1$\frac{1}{2}$ miles from junction with Trent & Mersey Canal. Concrete slipway into 2$\frac{1}{2}$' water suitable craft up to 24'LOA available 0800 -1900 daily by prior arrangement Tel Kidsgrove(07816) 5700. Fuel, parking for car and trailer (c), toilets, boatyard facilities. Exit from ramp requires tight turn so 4-wheel drive vehicles are most suitable. Charge and licence required.

Macclesfield Marina
Leave M 6 at junction 17 taking A 534, A 54 and A 523. Concrete slipway with 3$\frac{1}{2}$' water suitable craft up to 2' 10'' draft and 6' 10'' beam available 1000-1800 daily. Fuel, parking for car and trailer(c), crane, toilets, chandlery, boat and engine repairs. Further information Tel Macclesfield(0625) 20042.Charge and licence required.

Marineville Mooring, Lyme Road, Higher Poynton
From A 523 north of Macclesfield turn up Park Lane at Poynton traffic lights by the church: after 2 miles turn left into Shrigley Rd North then right into Lyme Rd by the Boar's Head: access is restricted to boats under 25'LOA. Concrete slipway with drop at end into min 2$\frac{1}{2}$' water available during daylight hours. Diesel, parking for car and trailer (c), toilets nearby, chandlery and boatyard facilities from Constellation Cruises Tel Poynton(0625) 873471 from whom permission to use the site must be obtained before crossing the canal bridge. Charge and licence required.

Lyme View Marina, Four Lane Ends, Adlington

From A 523 north of Macclesfield, turn east at Poynton lights into Dickens Lane/Street Lane, then Woods Lane. Steep concrete slipway into min 3½' water suitable craft up to 24'LOA available at all times. No fuel, parking for car and trailer. Further information Tel Poynton(0625) 4638. Charge and licence required.

Monmouthshire & Brecon Canal

The navigable length from Pontypool to Brecon, once the original Brecknock & Abergavenny Canal has been restored giving a cruising length of just over thirty three miles.

Red Line Boats, Goytre Wharf, Llanover

Leave M 4 at junction 26 taking A 4042 north and turning left at Llanover: (contact boatyard for advice on best route). Two concrete slipways, one steep and one gentle available during daylight hours. Fuel, parking for car and trailer (c), toilets, chandlery and boatyard facilites on site. Further information Tel Abergavenny(0873) 880516. Charge and licence required.

Montgomery Canal

This canal was planned to run northwards from Newtown and joined the Llangollen Canal at Frankton Junction. Parts of the canal have been restored but there are serious obstacles to complete restoration. Speed limit 4mph.

Pool Quay, Wern

Turn off A 483 north of Welshpool and over the old railway crossing: approach is via narrrow road and hump-backed bridge. Steep concrete slipway into min 3½' water available at all times and suitable small craft. Site gives acces to approx 7 miles of navigable canal. No fuel, parking for car and trailer. Purchase a BW sanitary key to gain access. No Charge.

Smithfield Car Park, Welshpool

Turn off A 483 by Spar into Church Street. Concrete slipway into min 3'water available at all times and suitable small craft. Site gives access to approx 1½ miles navigable canal. No fuel, parking for car and trailer (c). Purchase BW sanitary key to gain access. No Charge.

Oxford Canal

One of the earliest canals in southern England it was built to facilitate the transport of coal from the Warwickshire coalfield to Banbury and Oxford and thence the Thames. Now a very popular cruising waterway it runs for seventy seven miles from the junction with the Coventry Canal to Oxford and connects with the Grand Union Canal at Napton and Braunston.

Fenny Marine Ltd, Station Fields, Fenny Compton

Follow A 423 north from Banbury for 8 miles. Concrete slipway available from 0900-1700 daily. Fuel, parking for car and trailer (c), toilets, chandlery. Further information Tel Fenny Compton(029577) 461/2. Charge and licence required.

Napton Marina, Napton on the Hill, Stockton

Follow A 423 north from Banbury turning onto A 425 at Southam and following signs: site is 300yds south of the junction of the Oxford and Gd Union Canals. Concrete slipway available from 0900-1730 daily. Diesel, parking for car and trailer (c), winch, toilets, chandlery and full marina facilities. Further information Tel Southam(092681) 3644. Charge and licence required.

Rose Narrowboats Ltd, Stretton-under-Fosse

Leave M 1 at junction 20 taking A 427 west: site is on other side of canal necessitating transport across. Concrete slipway into max 2' water available during normal working hours suitable craft up to 65'LOA and 6' 10'' wide. Fuel, parking for car and trailer (c), chandlery and boatyard facilities on site. Further information Tel Rugby (0788) 832449. Charge and licence required.

Peak Forest Canal
This canal runs from the Ashton Canal at Ashton through Marple to Whaley Bridge and Buxworth and is fourteen miles long: it connects to the Macclesfield Canal at Marple Junction.

New Mills Marina, Hibbert Street

From central Manchester follow A 6 south to New Mills: site is 4 miles south east of Stockport. Concrete slipway available during daylight hours. Fuel ($\frac{1}{4}$ mile), parking for car and trailer (c), toilets, chandlery. Assisted launch available. Further information Tel New Mills(0663) 45000. Charge and licence required.

Rochdale Canal

Hebden Bridge Canal Basin, New Road, Hebden Bridge

Follow A 646 west from Halifax: access is controlled by lockable bollards and advance notice is required to use slipway Tel Hebden Bridge (0422) 842265. Concrete slipway available during daylight hours. Fuel ($\frac{1}{2}$ mile), parking for car and trailer nearby, toilets. Charge and licence required.

Sheffield & South Yorks Canal
This canal connects Sheffield to the River Humber via the Stainforth and Keadby Canal and the River Trent.

Tulleys Marine Services, Canal Basin, Sheffield

Site is in Canal Street opposite Exchange Place: access to site has only 13' headroom. Concrete slipway into min $3\frac{1}{2}$'water available by prior arrangement Tel Sheffield(0742) 731717. Fuel, parking for car and trailer (c), crane, winch, toilets, chandlery and boatyard facilities on site. Charge and licence required.

Staniland Marina, Lock Hill, Thorne

Leave M 18 at junction 6. Concrete slipway into 5' water available at all times. Fuel, parking for car and trailer, crane, toilets, chandlery and repairs on site. Further information Tel Thorne(0405) 813150. Charge and licence required.

Blue Water Marina Ltd, Thorne (Stainforth and Keadby Section)

Turn off M 18 at junction 6: site is opposite South Station. Concrete slipway into min $5\frac{1}{2}$' water available from 0800-1800 daily. Fuel, parking for car and trailer (c), crane, winch, toilets and showers, chandlery, berths, repairs. Further information Tel Thorne(0405) 813165. Charge and licence required.

Shropshire Union Canal
The canal connects with the Staffordshire and Worcester Canal at Autherley Junction and the Llangollen Canal at Hurleston junction before finally meeting the Manchester Ship Canal at Ellesmere Port. The Middlewich Branch of the canal connects the Shropshire Union to the Trent and Mersey Canal.

Countrywide Cruisers, The Wharf, Brewood

Leave M 6 at junction 12 taking A 5 west, turning off to Brewood: in village, turn right towards Bishop's Wood going over canal bridge and turning right immediately afterwards: site is $\frac{1}{4}$ mile down lane. Concrete slipway into 4' water available 0900-1700 (mon-fri only). Fuel, parking for car and trailer, toilets. Further information Tel Brewood(0902) 850166. Charge.

Holidays Afloat Ltd, Market Drayton
Site is by bridge on A 53. Concrete slipway into min 4' water available during working hours. Fuel, parking for car and trailer (c), chandlery. Further information Tel Market Drayton(0630) 2641. Charge.

Barbridge Marina, Wardle
Turn off A 51, 5 miles north of Nantwich: access has narrow bridge. Concrete slipway into 3' water available 0900-1800 daily or at other times by arrangement suitable craft up to 30'LOA. Fuel, parking for car and trailer (c), chandlery and boatyard facilities on site: assisted launch available. Further information Tel Wettenhall(027073) 682. Charge.

Venetian Marine, Cholmondeston (Middlewich Branch)
Leave M 6 at junction 17 taking A 534 to Nantwich then A 51 north: site is 1 mile from Barbridge junction. Concrete slipway into 4' water available 0900-1730 daily Tel Wettenhall(027073) 251. No fuel, parking for car and trailer (c), toilets, chandlery. Charge.

Staffordshire & Worcestershire Canal
A delightful cruising canal, it runs from Stourport-on-Severn, where it connects with the River Severn, to Great Haywood where it meets the Trent and Mersey Canal. Aldersley Junction and Autherley Junction connect it with the Birmingham and Shropshire Union Canals.

Ashwood Marina, Kingswinford
Follow A 449 south from Wolverhampton turning right after leaving Wall Heath and right at T junction. Concrete slipway into 4' water available during normal business hours and suitable craft up to 20'LOA and 6' 10'' wide. Fuel, parking for car and trailer, winch, toilets, engine servicing, chandlery. Further information Tel Kingswinford(0384) 295535. Charge.

Double Pennant Boatyard, Hordern Road, Wolverhampton
Site is close A 41 on west side of Wolverhampton. Steep concrete slipway into 3' water available 0900-1800 daily except mon by prior arrangement only and suitable boats up to 25'LOA, 6' 10'' wide and $2\frac{1}{2}$' draught. Fuel, parking for car and trailer (c), toilets, chandlery and boatyard facilities on site. Further information Tel Wolverhampton(0902) 752771. Charge.

Stratford-upon-Avon Canal
Built to connect Stratford-on-Avon to the expanding canal network, it meets the Worcestershire and Birmingham canal at Kings Norton, the Grand Union at Kingswood Junction and joins the River Avon in Stratford itself.

Earlswood Motor Yacht Club, Lady Lane, Earlswood
Follow A 34 north from Stratford-on-Avon turning left onto B 4102 and into Lady Lane after 2 miles. Concrete slipway available by prior arrangement only. Fuel, parking for car and trailer (c), toilets, moorings and clubhouse. Further information Tel Earlswood(05646) 2552. Charge.

Swallow Cruisers Ltd, Wharf Lane, Hockley Heath
Follow A 35 north from Stratford-on-Avon: site is 1 mile south of Hockley Heath. Concrete slipway into 2' water available 0830-1800 daily. Diesel, parking for car and trailer (c), toilets, chandlery and boatyard facilities on site. Further information Tel Lapworth(05643) 3442. Charge.

Trent & Mersey Canal
Running ninety three miles from Derwent Mouth to Preston Brook, the canal has junctions with nine other canals or canal branches and was an extemely successful waterway carrying china clay and flints for the pottery industry to The Potteries and taking away finished goods.

Dobsons Boatyard, The Wharf, Shardlow
Leave M 1 at junction 24 taking A 6 to Derby, turning off in Shardlow and following signs to the Wharf. Concrete slipway into 3½' water available 0830-1730 daily suitable boats up to 31'LOA and 3' draught. Fuel, parking for car and trailer (c), crane by arangement, winch, toilets, chandlery and all boatyard facilities on site. Further information Tel Derby(0332) 792271. Charge.

Shobnall Marina, Burton-on-Trent
Leave M 6 at junction 10 following A 461 and A 38 east taking B5017 to Shobnall. Concrete slipway into 3' water available during daylight hours. Fuel (diesel on site), petrol (300yds), parking for car and trailer(c), toilets, chandlery and boatyard facilities on site. Further information Tel Burton-on-Trent(0283) 42718. Charge.

Stenson Marina (Clayton Line Ltd), Stenson
Follow A 38 south from Derby taking A 5132 east to Twyford then follow minor roads. Concrete slipway available daily from 0900-1730 or at other times by arrangement Tel Burton-on-Trent(0283) 703113. Diesel, parking for car and trailer (c), toilets. Heavy towing equipment available. Charge.

Stone Boatbuilding Co, Canal Side, Newcastle Road
Turn off A 34 north of Stafford into Stone: site is by canal bridge. Concrete slipway available 0900-1800 (mon-sat) and 1000-1600 (sun) in summer. Fuel, parking for car and trailer (c), toilets, chandlery and repairs. Further information Tel Stone(0785) 812688. Charge.

Longport Boat Centre, Longport
Leave M 6 at junction 15/16 taking A 500, A 527 and B 5051. Steep concrete slipway into 2' water available 0900-1700 daily. Fuel, parking for car and trailer (c), toilets, chandlery and boatyard facilities on site. Further information Tel Stoke-on-Trent(0782) 813831. Charge.

Dolphin Boats, Old Whieldon Road, Stoke-on-Trent
From M 6 turn onto Queensway and then into Old Whieldon Rd. Concrete slipway into 2½' water available 0900-1800 daily and suitable boats up to 30'LOA. Petrol, parking for car and trailer (c), chandlery. Further information Tel Stoke-on-Trent(0782) 49390. Charge.

Union Canal (Scotland)
The canal is obstructed by road crossings but has reasonable cruising lengths. Speed limit 3mph: BW licence required. Further information from the Waterway Manager, Lowland Canals*.

Linlithgow to Broxburn (8 miles)

Manse Road Basin, Manse Road, Linlithgow
Follow B 9080 west from Edinburgh: site is near railway station. Concrete slipway 7'wide suitable craft up to 13'LOA. Fuel nearby, limited parking. No Charge.

East Church Street, Broxburn
Follow A 8 and A 89/899 west from Edinburgh: access is off East Main Street and site is near Sports Centre. Concrete slipway suitable for craft up to 25' LOA. Get key to gate from Sports Centre, East Main Street Tel Broxburn(0506) 854997. No Charge.

Lochrin Basin, Edinburgh to Slateford Aquaduct (3 miles)

Harrison Park, Edinburgh
Turn off A 70 Slateford Rd into Harrison Rd then into Harrison Gdns: site is on corner of Ashley Drive and Ogilvy Terrace. Small wooden ramp suitable boats up to 13'LOA. No fuel, parking for car and trailer in adjacent streets. This section is used regularly by rowers so take care to avoid them. No Charge.

Falkirk, Bantaskin to Glen Village through tunnel (1½miles)

Greenbank Road Slipway
Slipway 8'wide reached through Greenbank Rd car park available at all times. No Charge.

Worcs & Birmingham Canal
Part of the popular cruising circuit, the canal runs for thirty miles from Diglis in Worcester, where it connects with the River Severn to Kings Norton, where the Stratford-on-Avon canal enters, and ends in Birmingham.

Alvechurch Boat Centre, Scarfield Wharf
Leave M 5 at junction 5 taking A 38 and A 448 to Redditch: site is 4 miles north on the A 441. Concrete slipway available daily from 0800-1700 Tel(021) 145 2909. Fuel, parking for car and trailer (c), toilets, chandlery. Charge.

Sarabund Boat Centre, Hanbury Wharf, Droitwich
Leave M 5 at junction 5 taking A 38 to Droitwich town centre then B 4090 east for 2 miles: site is adjacent Eagle & Sun Inn. Concrete slipway into 6' water available during daylight hours and suitable boats up to 6' 10'' wide. Fuel, parking for car and trailer (c), Range Rover and driver available on request, toilets, chandlery and boatyard facilities on site. Further information Tel Droitwich(0905) 771018. Charge.

LAKE DISTRICT

Private craft are not allowed on the following lakes: Blea Tarn, Elterwater, Ennerdale Water, Haweswater, Little Langdale Tarn, Loughrigg Tarn, Loweswater, Rydal Water, Tarn Hows, Wastwater, Yew Tree Tarn. Powered craft (subject to speed limits) are permitted only on the following lakes: Coniston, Derwent Water, Ullswater and Windermere.

Coniston Water
Leave M 6 at junction 36 taking A 591 to Ambleside then A 593 to Coniston. The lake is in the Lake District National Park and is 5¼ miles long by ½ mile at its widest point: in places it is up to 180' deep. No powercraft may be launched from National Trust Land. There is a speed limit of 10mph on the lake.

Coniston Boating Centre, Lake Road
Turn down Lake Road between the garage and restaurant. Concrete and wood slipway available 0830-1800 weekdays in summer, 0900-1700 winter, (weekends by arrangement) Tel Coniston(0966) 41366. Fuel from garage in village, parking for car and trailer, winch, toilets, chandlers in Ambleside. Charge.

Light craft, but not powered craft can also launch from the car park at the north end of the lake or from the Old Brown Howe car park at the south west end of the lake.

Derwentwater
Leave M 6 at junction 40 taking A 66 west to Keswick. There is a speed limit of 10mph on the whole lake which is in the Lake District National Park. No powercraft may be launched from National Trust land.

Derwentwater Marina Watersports Centre, Portinscale
Turn off A 66 west of Keswick: site is on west shore of lake. Two concrete ramps into 3' water available from 0800-2200 daily Tel Keswick(0596) 72912. Fuel from Keswick (1 mile), parking for car and trailer (c), crane, toilets and showers, chandlery from Nichol End Marine, licensed club. Charge.

Keswick-on-Derwentwater Launch Company Ltd, Keswick
Launch over shingle from 0900-2130 (Mar-Nov) Tel Keswick(0596) 72263. No fuel, parking for car and trailer, toilets, chandlery from Nichol End Marine, Portinscale. Charge.

Nichol End Marine, Portinscale
Take first left turn after Keswick to Portinscale: ½ mile after village turn left into lane 300yds past Boat Club. Steel slipway into 4' water suitable craft up to 25'LOA. Petrol, parking for car and trailer (c), toilets, chandlery and boatyard facilities, boat hire, instruction and refreshments available. Further information Tel Keswick (07687) 73082. Charge.

Boats which can be manhandled may be launched from National Trust land near the B 5289, 2 miles south of Keswick opposite Barrow House Lodge by Ashness Gate. Launch light craft from car park at Kettlewell, ½ mile north of Lodore. No powercraft allowed.

Ullswater
Leave M 6 at junction 40 taking A 592. Speed limit on lake which is in the Lake District National Park is 10mph.

There are public launching sites, but not for powered craft, north of the steamer pier by the Willow Trees or at Glencoyne Bay 1 mile north near Glencoyne Bridge. Craft including powerboats can be launched at Howtown on the east side of the lake: access is via the B 5320 and the site is 3 miles south of Pooley Bridge; the site is suitable for craft up to 20'LOA.

The Spit, Glenridding, (Glenridding Sailing School)
Follow A 592 north from Windermere: access to site is via drive between the Ullswater
Hotel and the Glenridding Hotel. Launching over shingle beach available 1000-1700
Apr-Oct suitable sailing dinghies only. Fuel, car parking, leave trailers by arrrangement,
toilets and telephone. Launching is at the discretion of the owners and buoyancy aids
must be worn at all times. Further information Tel Pooley Bridge(076 84) 86601. Charge.

Lake Windermere
Leave M 6 at junction 36 taking A 591 to Windermere. The lake is 10½ miles
long and 1¼ miles wide at the widest point with 210' at the deepest point.
There is a speed restriction of 6 knots or 10 knots in certain areas but on much
of the lake water-skiing is allowed. All powered craft which use the lake are
required to be registered. Contact the Lake Warden at Ferry Nab Tel
Windermere(096 62) 2753 for further information.

Windermere Aquatic Ltd, Glebe Road, Bowness-on-Windermere
Assisted launching by yard staff only during normal business hours (1st Apr-31st Oct) Tel
Windermere(096 62) 2121/2. Fuel, parking for car and trailer (c), toilets, chandlery.
Charge.

Shepherd's Boatyard, Glebe Road, Bowness-on-Windermere
Concrete slipway available during normal business hours Tel Windermere(096 62) 3415.
Fuel nearby, parking for car and trailer (c) Charge.

Ferry Nab, Bowness-on-Windermere
Turn off A 592 Bowness to Newby Bridge road onto Hawkshead Ferry approach road:
access to site is through car park. Concrete slipway into min 4' water available 0800-
2200 (Apr-Oct) and 0900-1700 (Nov-Mar) and suitable all craft up to max 35'LOA and
4 tons. Fuel, parking for car and trailer (c), tractor assistance available (c), short term
moorings, toilets, telephone: chandlery and yard facilities nearby. Lake Warden's Office
is on site. Charge.

Waterhead, Ambleside
Boats of up to 20'LOA and 5 HP may be launched from the shingle beach here for a
charge.

Lowwood Hotel
Located 1 mile south of Ambleside on A 591. Use launching facilities only with permission
Tel Ambleside(05394) 33338. Charge.

Certain craft, but not powercraft, can be launched from shoreline owned by The National
Trust at the northern end of the lake. Contact The National Trust Tel Ambleside(0966)
33883. Charge.
Pay fee to:-
Millerground- Mr J W Cockman, Low Millerground, Windermere
Ferry House to Wray Castle - Mr A Longstaff, Harrowslack House, Far Sawrey.

There are also launching facilities available from 1st March to October at Fell Foot Park
near Newby Bridge, at the southern end of the lake, turning off the A 592. Contact The
National Trust Warden Tel Newby Bridge(0448) 31273. No cruisers over 19'LOA or
powered craft over 5HP are allowed. Parking for car and trailer.Charge.

Further sites for non-powered craft include:-

Buttermere - Follow A 66 west to Cockermouth, then B 5289 south: launch over beach
owned by the NT. Permission from Mrs T Richardson, Gatesgarth Farm, Buttermere or the
Kirkstile Inn, Loweswater. Charge.

Crummock Water - Follow A 66 west to Cockermouth then B 5289 south: suitable for canoes, windsurfers and small craft. Permission from Mrs R Beard, Rannerdale Farm, Buttermere. Charge.

Esthwaite Water - Follow B 5286 and 5285 from Ambleside. Launch rowing boats only from SW shore of lake. Permits from Hawkshead P O or Mr T W Taylor, Esthwaite Howe, Nr Sawrey Tel Hawkshead(096 66) 331.

Grasmere - Follow A 591 north from Windermere: launch canoes and sailing dinghies only from Easter to October. Permission from Mrs J M Allonby, Padmire, Pavement End, Grasmere Tel Grasmere(096 65) 409. Charge.

Talkin Tarn Country Club, Cumbria - Follow A 69 from Carlisle turning south onto the B 6413 at Brampton: site is 2 miles along this road and well signposted. Concrete slipway into min 1½'water available during daylight hours and suitable dinghies and trailer sailers only: powercraft are not allowed. Fuel (2 miles), parking for car and trailer nearby. Charge.

Thirlmere - Follow A 591 north from Windermere: launch over gravel beach at Armboth, details posted on site.

ADDITIONAL LAKE SITES

Clatto Country Park, Tayside
Follow A 923 from Dundee, crossing the A 972: at next roundabout turn right, then left and follow signs from Dalmahoy Drive. Launching into reservoir is available 1000-dusk (Apr-Sept): obtain day permit from Countryside Ranger who should be telephoned in advance Tel Dundee(0382) 89076. Charge.

Emberton Country Park, Olney, Bucks
From Northampton follow A 428 east, turning south onto A 509: site is south of Olney. Launching is available for sailing dinghies on purchase of a day permit. Further information Tel Bedford(0234) 711575. Charge,

Fairhaven Lake, Lytham St Annes, Lancs
Leave M 6 at junction 31 taking A 59/A 583 and A 584 west: site is east of Pier. Steep slipway into 3¼' water available daily from 0800-dusk and suitable canoes, dinghies and windsurfers: powerboats are not allowed. Fuel, parking for car (c), toilets. Contact Lake Manager for further information Tel Lytham(0253) 735439. Charge.

Ford (Loch Awe)
Turn off A 816 north of Lochgilphead onto B 840: site is at southern end of Loch Awe and access is via narrow roads. Launch from slipway belonging to Ford Motor Club, obtaining the key from the Ford Motor Hotel. Charge.

Holme Pierrepont (National Water Sports Centre), Nottingham
Follow signs from A 52, 3½ miles east of City centre. This lake is used for all types of watersports including dinghy and board sailing, water-skiing and power boat racing and launching is available during "shared use periods". Further information Tel Nottingham(0602) 866301. Charge.

Kielder Water, Northumberland
Follow M 6 and A 7 north turning east onto B 6357 at Canonbie and following minor roads. There are two large public slipways at Leaplish, half way along the south shore of the lake available for dinghies and trailer-sailers. Parking for car and trailer, dinghy park, toilets. Further information from the Warden Tel(0660) 50241. Charge.

Kinghorn Loch, Kinghorn, Fife
Approach from A 92 coast road: site is between Burntisland and Kinghorn and near Kinghorn Tannery. Launching available for dinghies and trailer-sailers at all times (no powerboats). Fuel, parking for car and trailer, chandlery from Lammerlaws Leisure in Burntisland. Obtain permission to launch in advance from Kirkcaldy DC, Town House, Kirkcaldy. No Charge.

Lake Bala, Gwynedd
Follow A 494 north from Dolgellau. Launching over hard beach available with permission at lakeside caravan site for sailing dinghies only. Contact Mr Anthony Pugh, Glanllyn, Llanuwchllyn. Charge.

Lake Clywedog, Nr Llanidloes, Powys
Follow A 44 east from Aberystwyth, turning onto B 4518 at Llanidloes. Lake is leased to Clywedog SC: launch sailing dinghies only with their permission. No fuel, parking for car and trailer, toilets. Contact Secretary, Mr P Dunsford, Pen-y-Bout, Cyfronydd, Welshpool. Charge.

Lochearnhead Watersports Centre, Loch Earn, Perthshire
Follow A 85 west from Perth: site is at junction with A 84 on shores of Loch Earn. Launching into 2' water available 0900-2100 suitable canoes, dinghies, windsurfers and water-ski boats. Petrol, parking for car and trailer (c), toilets. Further information Tel Lochearnhead (05673) 330. Charge.

Loch Ken Marina, Loch Ken
Follow A 713 north from Castle Douglas. Concrete slipway suitable for launching small craft. No fuel, parking for car and trailer, toilets. Charge.

Loch Lomond Marina, Balloch, Loch Lomond.
From Glasgow follow A 82 west: site is at southern end of Loch. Wooden slipway available 0900-1900 (summer), 0900-1700 (winter) or by arrangement. Diesel on site, petrol (100yds), parking for car and trailer (c), toilets and showers, chandlery, tractor, crane. No speed limit: water-skiing allowed. Further information Tel(0389) 52069. Charge.

Loch Tay, Kenmore Boatyard, Pier Road
Follow A 9 north from Perth, turning onto A 827: site is near head of loch. Slipway into about 3½' water available 0930- dusk and suitable craft with up to 3' draught. Petrol, parking for car and trailer, toilets, tractor. Speed limit 5mph in moorings. Premises of Loch Tay Boat Club are here and temporary membership of Club is available. Charge.

Monikie Country Park, Tayside
Take A 92 east from Dundee, turing left onto B 962 and follow signs. Launching available daily from 1000-dusk (Apr-Sept) on purchase of a permit. For further information contact the Contryside Ranger Tel Newbigging(038 235) 202. Charge.

Priorslee Lake, Priorslee, Telford
Turn off M 54 at junction 5. Lake is leased to Priorslee Lake Water Sports Assoc from whom permission to launch must be obtained. Site is suitable for sailing and powercraft. Contact the Secretary, Mr N Jones, Marina, 86a Church Road, Donnington Wood, Telford. Charge.

Rudyard Lake, Staffs
Turn off the A 523 Leek to Macclesfield road onto the B 5331 to Rudyard: at roundabout turn right and right again into Lake Road. The entrance to the site is approx 800yds down this road on the right. Two concrete slipways available at all times and suitable all non-powered craft. Fuel (½ mile), parking for car and trailer (c), toilets and telephone on site, nearest chandlers at Macclesfield Marina. Further information from the Lake Information Centre, Lake Rd. Charge.

Rutland Water, Oakham, Leics
Follow A 1 north turning onto A 606 at Stamford. Launching during daylight hours (1st Apr-30th Oct) daily is supervised by the Sailing Master who will inspect your craft. For further information contact the Reservoir Manager Tel Empingham(078 086) 321. Charge.

Salthouse Dock, Liverpool
Site is 100m off Inner Ring Road through the main entrance to the Albert Dock complex and gives access to approx 65 acres of water but with restricted headroom under bridges. Concrete slipway (1:8) into 5' water suitable dinghies (and powerboats at certain times only) available during daylight hours. No fuel, parking for car and trailer, toilets. Further information from Harbour Manager Tel(051) 2366090. Charge and licence required.

Strathclyde Country Park, Strathclyde Loch
Leave M 74 at junction 4 or 5 and follow signs. Concrete slipway into 8'water available 0930- dusk daily and suitable dinghies and powerboats. Fuel nearby, parking for car and trailer: the water sports centre has changing rooms and showers. Water-skiing is allowed in a restricted area and boat drivers must hold a Grade 2 licence: all slipway users must report to Booking Office before launching. Charge.

Tallington Lakes Leisure Park, Stamford, Lincs
Follow A 1 north turning onto A 16 at Stamford. Concrete slipway available 0800-2200 daily and suitable dinghies and powerboats. Fuel, parking for car and trailer (c), toilets, chandlery from Wentworth Sports and Leisure on site. Day visitors should telephone before arriving Tel Bourne(0778) 347000. Charge.

Willen Lake, Milton Keynes
Located just off Childs Way (H6): take junction 14 off M 1. Launching is available daily from 1000- dusk and is suitable for canoes, dinghies and windsurfers on purchase of a permit. Further information Tel Milton Keynes(0908) 670197. Charge.

Wyboston Watersports Centre, Wyboston, Beds
Follow A 1 north: site is at junction with A 45. Two concrete slipways into approx 5' water available 0700-1100 on weekdays only and suitable craft up to 19'LOA. Fuel ($\frac{1}{2}$ mile), parking for car and trailer, toilets, landrover (c). Further information Tel (0480) 213100. Charge.

USEFUL ADDRESSES

Basingstoke Canal Authority
Canal Office
Government Road
Aldershot GU11 2PS

British Waterways
Craft Licensing Office
Willow Grange, Church Road
Watford, Herts WD1 3QA
Tel Watford(0923) 226422

British Waterways Head Office
Melbury House, Melbury Terrace
London NW1 6JX
Tel(071) 725 8019

British Water Ski Federation
70 Brompton Road
London SW3 1EX
Tel(071) 584 8262

Broads Authority
Thomas Harvey House
18 Colegate
Norwich
Norfolk NR3 1BQ
Tel Norwich(0603) 610734

Cam Conservators
The Guildhall
Cambridge CB2 3QJ
Tel Cambridge(0223) 358977

Estates Office
Manchester Ship Canal Co
Trafford Road
Manchester Tel(061) 872 7031
(for Bridgewater Canal)

Forth Ports Authority
(Leith and Granton)
Tower Place
Leith, Edinburgh EH6 7DB
Tel(031) 554 4343/49

Grantham Canal Preservation Society
51 Winthorpe Road
Arnold
Notts NG5 74E

Gt Yarmouth Port and Haven Commissioners
21 South Quay
Gt Yarmouth NR30 2RE
Tel Gt Yarmouth(0493) 855151

Huddersfield Canal Society
General Secretary, R Dewey Esq
38 Paris Road
Scholes, Huddersfield HD7 1UA

Inland Waterways Assoc
114 Regents Park Road
London NW1 8UQ
Tel(071) 586 2556

Kings Lynn Concervancy Board
Common Staithe, Kings Lynn
Norfolk

Lake District National Park
Park Management and Visitor Services
National Park Office
Brockhole, Windermere
Cumbria LA23 1LJ
Tel Windermere(096 62) 6601

Lee Valley Park Authority
PO Box 88, Enfield
Middx Tel Lea Valley(0092) 717711

Lower Avon Navigation Trust
Mill Wharf, Mill Lane
Wyre Piddle
Pershore, Worcs WR10 1HW
Tel Pershore(0386) 552517

Middle Level Commissioners
Middle Level Offices
Dartford Road
March, Cambs PE15 8AF
Tel March(0354) 53232

National Trust Navigation Office
Dapdune Lea, Wharf Road
Guildford GU1 4RR
Tel Guildford(0483) 61389
(for River Wey and Godalming Navigations)

National Trust (North West Region)
Rothay Holme, Rothay Road
Ambleside, Cumbria
Tel Ambleside(05394) 33883

National Trust
36 Queen Annes Gate
London SW1 9AS
Tel(071) 222 9251

NRA (Anglian Region)
Kingfisher House
Goldhay Way, Orton Goldhay
Peterborugh PE2 O2R
Tel Peterborough(0733) 371811

NRA (Southern Region)
Vale Road
Tonbridge
Kent TN9 1XX
Tel Tonbridge(0732) 364922

NRA (Thames Region)
Kings Meadow House
Kings Meadow Road
Reading, Berks RG1 8DQ
Tel Reading(0734) 535000

Port of Bristol Authority
St Andrews Road, Avonmouth
Bristol BS11 9DQ
Tel Avonmouth(0272) 823681

Port of London Authority
Commercial Information Officer
Europe House, World Trade Centre
London E1 9AA
Tel(071) 481 8484

Port of Wisbech Authority
Port Office
Wisbech
Tel Wisbech(0945) 582125

Royal Yachting Assoc
RYA House, Romsey Road
Eastleigh, Hants SO5 47A
Tel Eastleigh(0703) 629924

Upper Avon Navigation Trust
Avon House, Harvington
Evesham, Worcs
Tel Evesham(0386) 870526

Waterways Manager
Aire and Calder Navigation
Locklane
Castleford WF10 2LH

Waterways Manager
Border Counties Waterways
Ellesmere
Shropshire SY12 9AA

Waterways Manager
Cheshire and Potteries
Chester Way
Northwich
Cheshire CW9 5JT

Waterways Manager
Coventry and Ashby Canals
Atherstone Road
Hartshill, Nuneaton
Warwick CV10 OTB

Waterways Manager
Crinan Canal
Pier Square
Ardrishaig
Argyll PA30 8DZ

Waterways Manager
East Midlands Navigations
24 Meadow Lane
Nottingham NG2 3HL

Waterways Manager
Grand Union South
Tring Office, Marsworth Yard,
Watery Lane, Marsworth
Nr Tring, Herts HP23 4LZ

Waterways Manager
Grand Union Central
Gayton Yard
Blisworth
Northampton NN7 3EF

Waterways Manager
Grand Union North
Canal Wharf, Derby Road
Loughborough, Leics LE11 OBX

Waterways Manager
Highland Canals
Canal Office
Clachnaharry
Inverness IV3 6RA

Waterways Manager
Kennet and Avon Canal
Bath Road
Devizes
Wilts SN10 1HB

Waterways Manager
Lancaster Canal
Aldcliffe Road,
Lancaster LA1 1SU

Waterways Manager
Lee and Stort Navigations
Enfield Lock, Ordinance Road
Enfield Middx EN3 6JG

Waterways Manager
Leeds and Liverpool East
Dobson Lock
Bradford
West Yorks BD10 OPY

Waterways Manager
Leeds and Liverpool West
Pottery Road
Wigan
Lancs WN3 5BB

Waterways Manager
London Canal
Top Locks, Poplar Avenue
Southall
Middx UB2 4PN

Waterways Manager
Lowland Waterways
Rosebank House
Main Street, Camelon
Falkirk SK1 4DS

Waterways Manager
Oxford Canal
Lock Cottage
The Dole
Priors Marston
Rugby CV23 8SS

Waterways Manager
Peak and Pennine Waterways
Vesta Street
Manchester M4 6DS

Waterways Manager
River Ouse
Naburn Lock
Naburn, York YO4 4RU

Waterways Manager
Severn Waterways
Llanthony Warehouse
Gloucester Docks
Gloucester GL1 2EH

Waterways Manager
S. Yorkshire and Chesterfield
Dun Street
Swinton
Mexborough S64 8AR

Waterways Manager
South Wales and Somerset Canals
The Wharf, Govilon
Abergavenny Gwent NP7 9NY

Waterways Manager
Staffs and Shropshire Union
Norbury Junction
Stafford ST20 OPN

Waterways Manager
Stratford and Grand Union
White House, Canal Lane
Hatton, Warwick CV35 7JL

Waterways Manager
Trent and Mersey Canal
Fradley Junction
Airewas
Burton-on-Trent
DE13 7DN

Waterways Manager
Worcester and Birmingham Canal
Canal Office, New Wharf
Tardebigge, Bromsgrove
Worcs B60 1NF

156